READING THE LANDSCAPE

MAY THEILGAARD WATTS

Naturalist,
The Morton Arboretum
Lisle, Illinois

READING THE

The Macmillan Company·New York
Collier-Macmillan Ltd., London

LANDSCAPE An Adventure

in Ecology

+ M,F

Seventh Printing 1967

Library of Congress catalog card number: 57-6359

For permission to quote from published material, thanks are due to the editors of *Ecological Monographs* and *The American Midland Naturalist;* also to Dr. William Albrecht, author of an article in *The Land*, and to the Chronica Botanica Company, publisher of Francis Ernest Lloyd's *The Carnivorous Plants*.

The Macmillan Company, New York
Collier-Macmillan Canada Ltd., Toronto, Ontario

For Raymond,
Erica, Nancy, and Tom

PREFACE

THERE is good reading on the land, first-hand reading, involving no symbols.

The records are written in forests, in fence-rows, in bogs, in play-grounds, in pastures, in gardens, in canyons, in tree rings.

The records were made by sun and shade; by wind, rain, and fire; by time; and by animals.

As we read what is written on the land, finding accounts of the past, predictions of the future, and comments on the present, we discover that there are many interwoven strands to each story, offering several possible interpretations.

Interpreting this reading matter, in place, on the land, seeing living things in their total environment, is an adventure into the field that is called ecology.

This ecology is a diverting traveling companion. It points out a bit of virgin prairie on a railroad right-of-way; it discovers the differing forests on north-facing and south-facing slopes; it finds evidence of long-dead Indian fires; it shows an island moving downstream; it interprets the changing shapes of evergreens, cattle, porches, and barns. It is an equally good companion for one staying at home. It finds a story in a schoolyard, in the corner of an old cemetery, in a foundation planting, and even in a window box.

The accounts offered here are intended to give the general reader an idea of the scope and application of ecology. Should they open gates into fields that seem alluring, further guidance may be found in the references at the end of each chapter. It happens that places where I have opened the book of the land are located in the Midwest, and in the mountains of the West and Southwest, areas familiar to me. I might have chosen other examples and other areas. The same reading techniques, with minor adaptations, will serve anywhere.

If these stories are good ones, if they show any breadth of vision, it is because I, as the narrator, am bestriding the shoulders of a giant, the wide and deep understanding of Doctor Henry C. Cowles, inspired teacher at the University of Chicago, great and first American ecologist. He taught me to read.

CONTENTS

ix

1.

IN SEARCH OF
ANTIQUES

or

The Forests of the Great
Smoky Mountains

WE FOUND, in the Great Smoky Mountains, the several antiques that were our goal.

For one of us the find was a woven bedspread.

For one the find was a song.

For another the find was a word.

For me the find was a forest.

The bedspread, the song, the word, the forest, had one quality in common. Each of them was not only an antique but also a disjunct. That is to say, each of them had been, long ago, cut off, isolated, or disjoined, from others of its kind.

The presence of disjuncts was to be expected there in the Smokies, the region that had so long been a sort of sanctuary, or refugium, for cut-off groups of plants and men and customs.

It was twilight when we entered the Smokies and we were eager

1

to reach our cabin before dark; but we, who had been stopped all the way across Indiana, Kentucky, and Tennessee by hanging lamps and melodeons, by Bennington ware and patchwork, could not fail to pull to the side of the road when an authentic floral antique shone white out of the dusk of the roadside woods.

A magnolia flower it was.

As I stood at the side of the hard modern road by the shiny modern automobile, and cupped the moonlight of the magnolia flower in my two modern prehensile hands, the warm June dusk around me seemed to brighten to a warm dawn—the dawn of flowering on the young earth. I could imagine the plash of broad reptilian feet behind me, and could pretend that I was seeing what no man ever saw, one of Nature's first experiments in producing a showy flower.

First things, beginnings, have fascination, and to anyone familiar with botanical literature, here was a first—the flower at the base of the "family tree" of flowers(11)*; the first tree in the book of Sargent's fourteen-volume "North American Silva"(12); the first family described in Pool's "Flowers and Flowering Plants"(11); the first family discussed in Arnold's "Paleobotany" (10) in the chapter Ancient Flowering Plants; the flower named for Pierre Magnol (1638-1715), professor of botany at Montpelier, who was the first to indicate the natural families of plants(12).

I looked long at the great white flower, and at the umbrella of broad leaves behind it, checking off the features that bespoke its antiquity among the flowering plants of the world today.

The petals, each one separated to its base, suggested that this was one of the world's earliest flower patterns. Petals of more modern flowers tend to be united along their sides.

The very way in which the flower fitted into my cupped hands was primitive. Such a wide open bowl does not tend to direct the path of an incoming insect visitor in any way. He may land, gather food, and take off, without depositing pollen on the sticky receptive

* Figures in parentheses refer to titles so numbered which will be found at the end of every chapter.

2

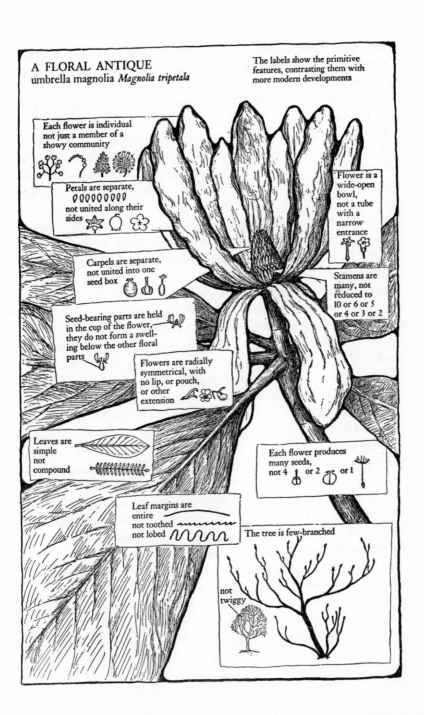

A FLORAL ANTIQUE
umbrella magnolia *Magnolia tripetala*

The labels show the primitive features, contrasting them with more modern developments

Each flower is individual not just a member of a showy community

Petals are separate, not united along their sides

Flower is a wide-open bowl, not a tube with a narrow entrance

Carpels are separate, not united into one seed box

Stamens are many, not reduced to 10 or 6 or 5 or 4 or 3 or 2

Seed-bearing parts are held in the cup of the flower, they do not form a swelling below the other floral parts

Flowers are radially symmetrical, with no lip, or pouch, or other extension

Leaves are simple not compound

Each flower produces many seeds, not 4 or 2 or 1

Leaf margins are entire not toothed not lobed

The tree is few-branched

not twiggy

surface that must receive it if the flower is to fulfill its destiny as a seed producer. In a later model the joined petals would form some sort of tube or jug, narrowed to a constricted entry-way that would route the incoming insect into contact with the sexual parts of the flower.

The large number of the pollen-laden stamens confirmed the evidence of the petals. In flowers that have developed united petals and constricted entry-ways, the production of pollen has been reduced and stamens have become so few that they can be counted on the fingers.

The many carpels forming a cone in the center of the flower, each one containing two potential seeds, these too were primitive. In a more recently evolved flower these would be combined into a single vessel to hold the seeds.

The loneliness of that great flower there in the dusk—that again was primitive. How different from the aggregate communities of minute flowers in the dandelion, or in the center of a daisy—as different as a mountain hermit from an assembled group of factory hands.

The leaves, large and plain, spoke of an outmoded pattern. Leaves even on oaks and sycamores, according to fossil records(10), were not so deeply lobed in the youth of the world as they are now. The very form of the little tree was primitive—if those paleobotanists are right who contend that primitive trees were few-branched. It stood, simple and uncomplicated, against the intricacy of its more twiggy associates.

One feature it lacked, an evergreen habit of the leaf, which is considered to be more primitive than the deciduous habit. Its relative, the great hard-leaved magnolia of the Gulf States, however, has this older feature added to the rest.

Magnolia relatives are abundant in Asia, living, and in Europe, dead, turned to stone. There are fossil magnolias in Greenland, too, and in Wyoming, and Portugal, but living, blooming ones only in Asia and parts of North America.

It was most fitting that we should be greeted first of all by

4

this flower as we entered the Great Smokies, haven of disjuncts.

This particular magnolia, *Magnolia tripetala*, was past its heyday of freshness. We were lucky to have seen it at all, in June. It began to come apart in my hands, and I completed its disrobing, carefully taking off, one by one, first the sepals, then the petals, and last the stamens. I wanted to see the floral formation that is considered reminiscent of the inflorescence of the ancient family of cycads, represented today by only a few fernlike or palmlike plants. In fact, the entire floral pattern of the magnolia has much similarity to the pattern shown in fossils of the now wholly extinct cycadeoids (10).

The flower and the last of the daylight were both gone. Antique-hunting was over for that day.

Early next morning we were off again, on the search for an antique forest.

It was as if we were hunting through an "old curiosity shop" that had stood firm through the years, quietly carrying on business at the old stand while civilizations of plants and animals shifted or swept by entirely.

In the attic of this forest "antique shop" was a unique exhibit, living quarters of a bygone age, preserved intact.

We stepped into that exhibit so suddenly that it seemed unreal. A few yards away from a teeming parking area at Newfound Gap, we had simply walked a short piece along the Appalachian Trail, and found ourselves plunged into antiquity.

Massive boles of hemlock and red spruce uplifted their durable canopy into a blue mist. Their dark boughs dripped with mist and moss. Broken raindrops, shattered by layer after layer of needles, and enmeshed in webs of moss draperies, sank soundlessly into the deep receptive green of club moss, lichens, liverworts, and oxalis leaves.

This forest told a story of cold and ice pushing down over the northern hemisphere, driving vegetation southward. Here, it was the vegetation of New England and eastern Canada that was forced down into the Smokies.

When the cold retreated, these evergreens were crowded out of the lower places, crowded out (as evergreens seem ever destined to be from the more modern situations by the more modern flora), until only the mountaintops were left to them. Probably this forest climbed up from the lower parts of the Smokies, to take over the ridges only after the cold had ameliorated enough so that there was no longer a timber line this far south. "Relicts," these left-behind plants are called. There they stand, thriving massively, in the daily dripping mists, and associating with plants that were native to the region long before this northern infiltration took place.

We had found an antique forest, and we spent the day richly within it; but we were not content, any more than one who was looking for a tomb of the Pharaohs would be satisfied with a Victorian parlor. We were looking for greater antiquity than that of the glacial period.

The story of the mountains is long, starting with deposition under water, then continuing through upheavals and uplifts, and slow ages of erosion. The vegetation of the Smokies offers records, not only of this local heaving, but also of changes and separations in other parts of the world, changes that have resulted in leaving many stranded or dispossessed plants in the sheltering arms of these mountains.

The breaking of the old land bridge to Eurasia is one such ancient event that is recorded here in the Smokies. That record is found in so-called "paired species" of plants. No two are exactly alike, but many differ only slightly, as might be expected when connections are broken off and close relatives are permanently segregated. Among such paired species are our ironwood, *Ostrya virginiana*, and the European hornbeam, *Ostrya carpinifolia;* our wood anemone, *Anemone quinquefolia,* and the European wood anemone, *Anemone nemorosa;* our wild lily of the valley, *Maianthemum canadense,* and the European *Maianthemum bifolium;* and many others. The American member of each pair is growing today in association with plants such as the tulip tree, sassafras, magnolia, witch-hazel—plants whose ancestors were eliminated from Europe when the glacial cold drove them south, and the mountaintop cold of east-west mountains stopped their retreat.

The breaking of the old land bridges to Asia, and to Greenland, is recorded in the presence of plants growing here and in eastern Asia today, and occurring as fossils in Greenland. The tulip tree is such a plant.

The list of plants in eastern America and eastern Asia, but not in Europe, is long. It includes the genera of our sweet gum, *Liquidambar*, and of our mayapple, *Podophyllum*; of *Trillium*, *Catalpa*, *Phlox*, *Jeffersonia*, and many others(4).

Famous botanists have long focused their thoughts on this problem of distribution. The naturalist, Louis Agassiz, linked the distribution to parallel development under similar conditions. Asa Gray connected the present distribution with ancient migrations under climatic changes. He said, "I cannot imagine a state of circumstances under which the Siberian elephant could migrate, and temperate plants could not." It was Sir Joseph Hooker who realized that of all plants that migrated southward before the glacier, those in eastern America and eastern Asia were the only ones that did not meet adversity in the form of mountain barriers.

The previous existence of a warmer climate is suggested by the presence of a few plants whose relatives are largely in the tropics. Silverbell, *Halesia;* pawpaw, *Asimina;* and fringe tree, *Chionanthus*, are examples of this group.

The story of the uplift of the western mountains, and their drying effects on the prevaling westerlies is recorded in the presence here of plants that are found as fossils in Wyoming (1) and elsewhere along the shores of the western sea that once cut America in two; beech, walnut, hackberry, elm, and persimmon were a few of the members of the widespread forest that were driven out by drought.

Certainly individual antiques such as these were abundant enough to satisfy almost any antique hunter. But we were far from satisfied. We wanted to step into a forest of the Tertiary period, a forest intact. It might have seemed like an unachievable goal (as if some antique hunter in a shop had looked up from old crayon portraits and flower prints and demanded to see a cave man in the act of painting bison on the walls of his cave) if we had not read about the actual existence of such a forest here in the Smokies.

It was along the Alum Creek Cave trail that we stepped back over the intervening ages, into that ancient forest.

Suddenly we were in a forest of the opera backdrop, of storied tapestries, of blue-green, fairy-tale illustration.

Unchanged, it had survived while mountains bulged and crumbled; unchanged, while mammals grew and reptiles shrank; unchanged, while prairies spread, and teeth and hooves grew hard; unchanged, while man learned to make fire, and pots and cloth, and war.

Unchanged? Not entirely. There was a great change in the extent of this forest. Once it spread around the world. But after the land bridges were broken, the western mountains uplifted, and the glacial cold had pushed down, this forest in the southern Appalachians was all that was left in America. Stretches of it remained in the Cumberland Mountains, and small, rich remnants of it survived in the sheltered coves of the Smokies.

One other major change had come to the forest. Some of the trees of antiquity, when the forest was widespread, have persisted in distant parts of the world, but are not found here. Others have remained the same throughout the centuries.

We walked gratefully where dignified boles lifted the canopy high to make a timeless green shade that urged the saplings below into a similar dignity. The understory plants held their foliage flat and broad, like begging hands that caught each green-gold strand of sunshine.

By the time the understory of small trees and the third story of shrubs had entangled each thread of light, it was only an occasional frayed wisp that dangled down to touch the forest floor. But out of those frayed wisps the forest floor had woven itself a garment that enfolded everything in richness.

The most beautiful single aspect of the entire forest was, surely, the insteps of the trees. A more suitable union of tree and earth could hardly exist. Those arched and clutching roots wore lichens and mosses, liverworts, ferns, and fungi, tucked into crannies, enshrouding curves, and lushly molded to muscular bulges.

This richness of growth covered any bark characteristics at the base of the trees until you might think that the trees were all of one kind. But all of one kind they decidedly were not—nor of two kinds, nor of a few kinds. Nowhere in America could one see so many different kinds assembled in one natural forest.

What should this forest be called(6)?

We, who were accustomed to forests named for their dominant trees, such as oak-hickory, beech-maple, or spruce-fir, could not find here any two trees dominant enough to give their names to this formation.

We went that day, and on succeeding days, to several cove forests. Always we found this rich assortment of many kinds of trees. The ones that seemed to be most abundant in the canopy were basswood (the white basswood, *Tilia heterophylla*, not the basswood of our northern deciduous forest), sugar maple, sweet buckeye, tulip tree, yellow birch, beech, and hemlock. Somewhat less abundant were red oak, bitternut hickory, white ash, and cucumber magnolia.

The most surprising member of the association was *Halesia*, the silverbell. We had met it often, but only as a shrub. Here it attained the stature of a tree.

In some areas of the cove forests, certain trees appeared to be dominant; but we would no sooner decide on the name "silverbell" forest for example, than the character of the forest would change and weave its elements into a new pattern of "beech-hemlock" or "tulip-hemlock-dead chestnut."

It soon became easy to understand why certain ecologists have coined a new sort of name for this rich mixture, calling it the "Cove Hardwood Complex," or the "Mixed Mesophytic Association." The latter phrase is taken directly from E. Lucy Braun's "Deciduous Forests (1). Her concept of the forests of the southern

Appalachians is the chief basis for the ideas of the Smokies as set forth here.

We dallied in the coves, sitting on mossy bulges to inspect the markings in the throats of flowers with our hand lenses, and to trace plants unknown to us, through botanical keys to identification.

Insects came to rest, now and then, on the moss, the leaves, the pages of our books. They seemed to move as lazily as we did in the green shade. Identify them we could not, except as further additions to our antique finds. A recent "Study of Summer Foliage Insect Communities in the Great Smoky Mountains"(7) shows that the insects of the coves tend to be primitive ones.

"So to the moist, productive, ancient environment of the cove forests is matched a nematoceran-dominated, productive, primitive, and moderately-diverse foliage insect community.

"It is suggested that the primary correlation of modernity is with drying power of the atmosphere. It is suggested that primitive insects with relatively delicate body coverings and unspecialized respiratory apparatus are less able to withstand a dry-hot environment than more advanced and more specialized insects"(7).

Perhaps it was not an illusion that these insects around us did not buzz so busily as do our northern Illinois insects. Another study(14) concludes that more modern, more active insects tend to appear in environments of high energy intensity—midday, midsummer, and the tropics—and more primitive insects in environments of low energy intensity.

I was knee-deep in mosses, hunched over a hand lens, when a voice behind me asked, "Well, found *Shortia* yet?"

A smiling stranger had paused on the path behind us to ask that question, the famous question that had been passed from botanist to botanist in these mountains in the 1840's, when many had joined in the search for this lost plant.

The story of *Shortia* starts in 1781, when André Michaux, outstanding French botanist, landed in America to collect plants for His Majesty Louis XVI, to add to the already fabulous gardens at Versailles. Incidentally, one can hardly enter the Smokies without being conscious of Michaux. Stretches of the highway are lined with the delicately-foliaged tree *Albizzia*, one of his spectacular gifts from Asia by way of Europe. Certainly one cannot use a botanical key without being well aware of Michaux, because so many of the plants have the abbreviation "Michx." following the scientific name, indicating that he was the first to describe the plant in question(9).

A herbarium of pressed specimens went back to France with Michaux. At the end of the collection were plants labeled "*plantae ignotae.*" And among those unknowns, unidentified for half a century, was a small specimen without flowers, bearing only leaves and fruit.

In 1839 Asa Gray, later a natural history professor at Harvard, came to France to look at Michaux's herbarium. That sheet, without a name, without a flower, caught his attention. He realized that this was a real find, a new plant—not only a new species, but a new genus. Having been first to recognize the plant as a new genus, he was entitled to name it. He decided to call it "*Shortia*" for his botanical friend, Doctor Charles Wilkins Short.

In 1840 when Gray returned to America, botanists began a long-continued hunt for this plant.

Gray described the flower as he thought it should be, on the basis of the fruit. One day, looking through an old Japanese herbal, his attention was suddenly caught by a familiar form in one of the woodcuts. Then he realized that he was looking at leaves that were scalloped and shaped and veined like the leaves of Michaux's pressed specimen. And the flowers depicted with them were much as he had predicted they would look.

Botanists pursued their hunt, now with better knowledge of what to look for, but the plant was not found until ninety-eight years after Michaux had first seen it. So ended the historical quest for the lost antique(13).

The extreme and apparently increasing rarity of shortia may be a mark of an old species, probably on the verge of extinction;

or it may be due to the fact that its seeds have no arrangement for dispersal(2).

No, we did not find the antique named *Shortia galacifolia*, or Oconee bells. But we found plenty of plants with "Michx." appended to their scientific names; and one plant with "Michx.f." appended. The "f." records the fact that Michaux's son, designated "Michaux fils," had come to this country to botanize in the footsteps of his father.

As we hunted out the lush coves, we crossed intervening slopes and hollows that held other types of forest, each forest made up of parts of the Mixed Mesophytic Association. It was as if we saw individual facets of the jewel that was a rich cove forest. In another sense, it was as if, from the richly and intricately woven fabric of the coves, a few strands had been drawn off into a heavy tassel here, or a coarsely woven net there, or a fringe on another side, or a few tattered threads where the wear was great.

In still another sense, it was as if the Mixed Mesophytic Association of the coves was an imposing organization, having within it several committees on specialized activities. One such committee might have been called "Committee in Charge of North-facing Slopes." It was dominated by beech and sugar maple, and reminded us of Warren's Woods near Three Oaks, Michigan.

Another forested area might have been called "The Committee in Charge of Sheltered North-facing Slopes Along a Deep Valley." This situation was dominated by beech; in fact, most of the trees were beeches. We were reminded of a forest at Turkey Run State Park, in Indiana.

On southerly slopes of lower altitudes, dead chestnuts, hemlocks, and tulip trees were prominent. One slope, thick with sugar maple, was reminiscent of the north-facing side of a ravine in the Morton Arboretum.

A low knob with oaks and blueberries might have been part of the older dune area in Indiana, or a part of the Ozarks.

Again, a ridge with oak and hickory might have been back home at the edge of the prairie.

Altitude, or exposure, or soil, has selected the strands of the cove forests that are woven into each of the outlying forests.

These selected strands of the cove fabric, or facets of the cove jewels, or committees of the cove forest organization—whatever we choose to call them—have been given the name of "Mixed Mesophytic Association segregates"(6).

Each segregate we saw seemed to be a sample of a forest somewhere outside of this southern Appalachian area.

Here no vacationer need be homesick long. If he comes from eastern Asia he can sit on a heath bald under great rhododendrons; if he comes from the Great Lakes area, he can find his forest of beech-maple-hemlock; if he comes from the prairie's edge, he can seek out a dry southerly slope and hobnob with oaks and hickories; if he longs for Canada, he can climb up among the spruces and firs.

We started home, even more full of antique-talk than when we arrived. The one of us who had bought a bedspread told that it was the "Whig Rose pattern," a disjunct pattern, brought to the Smokies long ago by pioneers for whom the word "Whig" had a meaning, and handed down through generations long after the meaning was forgotten.

Another one of us said she had heard an antique word. She had not succeeded in hearing any of the Shakespearian words said to have been brought to the mountains long ago, and to have suffered little change. But as she was talking with a woman on a porch between an old hand loom and a new washing-machine, the fox terrier had barked; and the woman had said to it, "Feeling feisty, aren't you?" Alberta Hannum had written(3): "Out of Chaucer comes their word 'feisty,' meaning impertinent."

The antique-song collecting had come close to being a failure. Certainly no one had heard the one song that we most desired to hear since reading that John Jacob Niles had heard a Holiness preacher singing it, the song that had been "recorded only once before in modern times, by Ralph Vaughan Williams in England" (3).

13

That song was "Down in yon forest hall, Sing May, Queen May, Sing Mary." But we did hear a boy and girl in an old Ford on a mud road singing "Barbara Allen"; and, in spite of the fact that very possibly it may have been taught to them by a music teacher from New England, we were satisfied. That durable ballad, woven of threads from English and Scottish ballads, "Bonny Barbara Allen," and threads of North Carolina mountain life, might perhaps have entered these mountains along with the pattern for the Whig Rose coverlet.

Talking of antiques and disjunct weaving, and words, and songs, and plants, and forests, we left the mountains, starting northward toward home.

We were traveling northward as the deciduous forest had traveled from the refugium of the southern Appalachians when the glacier retreated.

We stopped to look at forests. It was plain to us now that a new element was shaping their assemblage. Plants continued to be eliminated by soil, and by exposure, but altitude was of little importance. Latitude was becoming increasingly important. The cold finger of frost was laid on species after species.

By the time we reached the famous Cox Woods near Paoli, Indiana, the linden of the southeast had been eliminated, and the sweet buckeye, *Aesculus octandra*, was gone. So was *Halesia*, and fringe tree, magnolia, and sourwood, and many others. Beech and sugar maple had become more prominent.

We walked long among those well-born trees of proud stature, remembering that this type of forest had once extended across Indiana and Ohio, and had worn out many an axe, many a saw, many a pioneer, before it had been wiped out in favor of corn and wheat.

Then we moved northward again, watching latitude do its work, not only on plants, but also on the number of porches and rocking chairs, and chewing-tobacco signs; and Baptist churches.

As we swerved toward the west, the effect of the Rocky Mountains began to enter the picture. Added now to the influence of soil, exposure, and latitude, was the high-evaporation ratio. Beech and flowering dogwood dropped out of the picture; oaks, oaks, oaks, took their places, with a little hickory. We had seen this forest on a dry slope in the Smokies.

Presently, fingers of prairie began to pry into the oak woods—and we were back home, unloading our antiques and our memories of antiques.

REFERENCES

1. *Deciduous Forests of Eastern North America* by E. Lucy Braun. Blakiston, Philadelphia, 1950.
2. *Foundations of Plant Geography* by Stanley A. Cain. Harper, New York, 1944.
3. *The Great Smokies and the Blue Ridge; The Story of the Southern Appalachians*, edited by Roderick Peattie. Vanguard, New York, 1943.
4. "Certain Floristic Affinities of the Trees and Shrubs of the Great Smoky Mountains and Vicinity" by Stanley A. Cain. *Butler University Botanical Studies* 1 (September, 1930), 129-156.
5. "A Biological Spectrum of the Flora of the Great Smoky Mountains National Park" by Stanley A. Cain. *Butler University Botanical Studies* 7 (April, 1945), 11-24.
6. "The Undifferentiated Forest Climax and the Association Segregate" by E. Lucy Braun. *Ecology* 16 (July, 1935), 514-519.
7. "A Study of Summer Foliage Insect Communities in the Great Smoky Mountains" by R. H. Whittaker. *Ecological Monographs* 22 (January, 1952), pp. 1-44.
8. "The Great Smoky Mountains—Their Geology and History," by Philip B. King and Arthur Stupka. *Scientific Monthly* 71 (July, 1950), 31-49.
9. "Summer Key to the Trees of Eastern Tennessee" by R. E. Shanks and A. J. Sharp. *Journal of the Tennessee Academy of Science* 22 (April, 1947), 114-137.
10. *An Introduction to Paleobotany* by Chester A. Arnold. McGraw-Hill, New York, 1947.
11. *Flowers and Flowering Plants* by Raymond Pool. McGraw-Hill, New York, 1941.
12. *The Silva of North America; A Description of the Trees Which Grow Naturally in North America Exclusive of Mexico*, by Charles Sprague Sargent. Houghton Mifflin, Boston, 1947.

13. "Asa Gray and His Quest for *Shortia galacifolia*" by Charles F. Jenkins. *Arnoldia* 2 (April 10, 1942), 13-36.
14. "Evolutionary Level in Relation to Geographic, Seasonal, and Diurnal Distribution of Insects," by Clarence Hamilton Kennedy. *Ecology* 9 (October, 1928), 367-379.
15. "The Tertiary Character of the Cove Hardwood Forests of the Great Smoky Mountains National Park" by Stanley A. Cain. *Torrey Botanical Club Bulletin* 70, 213-235.
16. "Vegetation in the Great Smoky Mountains" by R. H. Whittaker. *Ecological Monographs* 26 (January, 1956), 1-80.

2.

PRAIRIE PLOWING
MATCH

or

The Making and Breaking
of the Tall Grass Sod

THERE was not a "Whoa!" to be heard at the Plowing Match this year.

Farmers, especially the older farmers, talked about that.

They talked about several sounds, and sights, and smells, that were missing. Not because they were suddenly missing—there was no drastic change this year—but because this year's match was the

Seventy-fifth Anniversary of the Wheatland
Plowing Match
with
Special Festivities
and
Special Exhibits of Old-time Machinery,

people's thoughts tended to turn backward.

17

There was a lone plowman with a walking plow and two horses. But he was carved on granite, on the newly erected marker at the corner of the farm where the matches were being held.

All comers stepped up briskly to inspect the new marker, and then lingered to talk of the past.

Our family had driven to the Plowing Match, as we have been in the habit of driving on the morning of the second Saturday of each September, down a straight road that crosses the section lines at right angles and offers a clear view to the flat horizon.

Such a surface is to be expected, of course, on the way to a Plowing Match taking place in a township named *Wheatland*, near one town called *Plainfield* and another called *Plano*.

We had time to inspect the new marker while the plowmen were having their "drawing for lands."

"This, to me, is Illinois," rolled out a seasoned voice beside me, and I turned to see one of our local politicians making an inclusive gesture with his cigar.

My eyes followed the arc of his gesture.

"Illinois? *Just exactly where?*" I wondered.

Not the granite marker. That was Vermont.

Not the expensive evergreen planting that had been hastily installed. That consisted of Mugo pine from the mountains of Switzerland.

Not the big basket of garden flowers set at the base of the marker (evidently one of the entries in the Flower Show of the

Ladies' Fair). The flowers were marigolds and zinnias and dahlias, whose ancestors all came to us from Mexico, by way of Europe, where they went to finishing school; and petunias from South America; and gladioli from South Africa.

Not the sparrow that alighted long enough to mark the marker. He was English.

Not the freshly clipped grass at our feet. That was bluegrass from Eurasia.

Not the weeds in the grass. They were chiefly dandelions and plantain (said to have been called "white-man's foot" by the Indians), both from Europe.

Prairie plowing match—
chiefly foreigners going under

Not the plowmen who were driving their tractors onto the field. They, too, were sons or grandsons of Europeans.

I glanced further off.

Not that Norway spruce in front of the nearest farmhouse, nor the European larch beside it.

Not those lilacs from Asia Minor.

Not the Black Angus cattle from Scotland.

Not even the small pin oaks and honey locusts recently planted along the highway. They are native further south in Illinois, but not here.

But yes, the two tall cottonwoods and the line of willows in the drainage ditch—these are natives in this area. But even they had come in recently, only after men had dug the ditch.

The plowmen were beginning, slowly, painstakingly, to turn the important opening furrows, establishing a straight line and setting the required depth—between five and six and a half inches—no more, no less. Presently they were making the important return furrow, folding a ridge to meet the first one exactly and to cover all trash.

There was one plowman who looked back and shook his head because a line of foxtail grass, another European invader, showed clearly down the entire length of the opening furrow. On the next plot a pigweed stuck out its thick green European tongue between the black furrows. On all the plots, we could watch foreigners being turned under; barnyard grass, alsike clover, timothy, red clover, English plantain, yellow sweet clover, Canada thistle. There was an occasional native going under, chiefly ragweed and smartweed.

We went over to watch the plowman Graeme Stewart at work; he was National Level Land Champion, the second national champion from Wheatland. There were neither natives nor foreigners sticking up out of his shapely furrows—just folded satin blackness.

Still searching for Illinois, we wandered toward the farmyard where tents and counters had been set up.

We passed a prize tall corn plant, tied to a Scotch pine. Its tassels were up among the orange branches where starlings from Europe were noisy. We inspected the prize-winning vegetable exhibit. It contained pumpkins, popcorn, squash, yams, beets, beans, watermelons, peas, lima beans, tomatoes, turnips. Nothing there was Illinois.

Tied to a post was an 18-foot sunflower plant with its great head hanging. A "Russian Sunflower" it was labeled; but here was a descendant, at least, of a native—a descendant of the wild sunflower of the prairies, hybridized, selected, and named in Europe it is true, but now returned, tall and big-headed to look down over garden fences upon its wild relatives.

We bought a souvenir program and went in under the big tent

20

From that time on, crops reached down deeper, and took out more, from the rich storehouse of the prairie.

Fifty-ninth Match——1935
This was the first year in the history of the Wheatland Plowing Match in which no horse-drawn plows were entered, all being tractor drawn.

And so the work of these grasslands was no longer to be done by the animal that had evolved with the developing of the world's grasslands. It was when the rising continents, with their drier and colder conditions, made grasslands where had been forests and swamps, that the horse developed longer legs, concentrating their weight on the one central toe, and gaining strength from the keeled-and-grooved joints that replaced ball-and-socket joints. These legs made possible a longer stride and increased speed over smooth ground. The longer head and longer neck probably developed simultaneously, making it possible for the long-legged animal to graze. Along with the development of the harder, drier foods of the plains, came the horse's elongated tooth crowns, with their hard projecting ridges of enamel backed inside by dentine and outside by cement.

George Gaylord Simpson(20) says:

These horses were learning to eat grass and acquiring the sort of teeth . . . that enabled them to do so. They were changing over from browsing animals to grazing animals, still herbivorous but with a profound change in their way of life. It is not likely to be a coincidence that at the same time grass became common, as judged by fossil grass seeds in the rocks.

The 1935 Plowing Match saw the end of power that came from the land and was returned to the land as fertilizer.

Fifty-third Match——1929
Six weeks drought before the match baked the ground and made plowing most difficult.
Forty-sixth Match——1922
Unprecedented drought and intense heat made conditions for plowing about as bad as had ever been experienced and greatly reduced the attendance at this match.

But the Indians and the buffaloes and the big bluestem grass could have told that the drought was *not* unprecedented.

Thirty-third Match——1909
Alvin Stark was disqualified, because his horses became unmanageable, having been frightened by the sight and noise of automobiles arriving for the match.

Probably the furrows that Alvin Stark's unmanageable horses plowed were curves that were much more native to the prairie than the straight lines and mathematical right angles that men have superimposed on its face.

Thirty-first Match——1907
The Wheatland Match had now become the political forum and jousting grounds for the northern section of the state. All candidates and important office-holders from near-by counties were on hand for each match.

But they were not plowing.

It was the accumulated black riches of the old prairie that caused the gathering of parasites, as accumulated riches cause the gathering of parasites everywhere. I remember the mountain-top tundra. There were no accumulated riches there. And there was not apparent a single parasite, saprophyte, or even a clinging vine.

Thirtieth Match——1906
Interest of the crowd was divided between the skilled plowmen, and an innovation to the match, a great steam-drawn gang plow, which turned ten furrows at a time. It was likened to a Mississippi river steamer, plowing up waves, as it went down the field.

As plowing was made easier and easier, more and more Illinois soil would be drained away, until Mississippi river steamboats would, in time, actually be plowing through waves of prairie soil, but they would not need to leave the Mississippi to find that soil.

Twenty-eighth Match——1904
Interest was drawn to earliest models of the "horseless buggy" a few being seen at the match.

24

Bumping across the ruts toward the Plowing Match, without benefit of filling stations, or numbered roads, or even "Blue Books," those first "horseless buggies" drew behind them, across the face of the prairie, the first string of a network of roads whose strands were to increase in width, number and strength, and enmesh an ever-increasing number of foreigners, both plant and animal.

Fourteenth Match——1890
Over 1000 rigs and vehicles were hitched along the fences and around the barns.

What kind of fences?

Osage orange

They might have been the then recently invented barbed wire (1874). The invention put bounds to the seemingly boundless prairie. It enabled farmers to move farther west. A handbook for emigrants from the East, in 1835, said, "Much of this land must lie unoccupied for generations for want of fencing."

On the Illinois prairie the coming of barbed wire meant the gradual grubbing out of miles of Osage-orange hedge.

Seventh Match——1883
The weather was hot and dry, and the fields were hard and packed. Great interest was shown in the riding-plow events, because farmers were realizing that everything should be done to free themselves and their sons from the more arduous work of the farm.

Each change that made plowing easier, even the change from walking to riding, extended plowland further into the prairie.

Sixth Match——1882
> The season had been very dry and it was hard plowing for the contestants.

It was this sort of summer that had sent prairie roots deep, deep down, long before plowing matches had been thought of, or plows.

Second Match——1878
> Hot dry weather had baked the ground extremely hard. Good plowing under adverse conditions resulted. Wm. Castles won the highest prize, a pair of silver-mounted bridles.
> Ladies were invited this year, and brought picnic lunches, and over 500 enjoyed the noonday meal in a beautiful grove near the field on which the match was held.

Those same "adverse conditions" had long ago determined the winners among plants on the prairie. The winners were the ones we now call "native." Those conditions had probably determined also the kind of tree that would furnish shade for the ladies when they opened those picnic baskets. A stand of trees given the name "grove" at that period was usually composed of bur oaks.

The First Match—1877
> The committee reported concerning this match: We learned among other things that a furrow can be plowed straight; that there are men who are masters of the plow; that while we live we progress; that sulky plowing is a great step in advance of all hand plowing.
> Factory representatives of plows were on hand with their latest models. Sulky plows were new, and were tested for merit on the grounds.

All the contestants walked, but they dreamt of riding in one of those modern sulkies some day. This innovation would enable them to extend their plowland farther into the prairie, and leave them more time for digging ditches and building fences.

There was probably an occasional purple turkey-foot (the seed-spike that gave the name "turkey-foot" to the big bluestem grass) reaching out from the unsuccessful furrows at that first match, if any puny specimens were left as survivors of former plowings.

At the far end of the field, in a corner that was too hard to plow, the six-foot high bluestem, or turkey-foot, may have whisked the flies from the horses as they made the turn. A prairie chicken probably flew off here, or a whole covey of quail there, or an upland

Europe

One foot of Illinois

Central America

plover, or a flock of passenger pigeons that had paused to rest or to glean a few seeds.

We had finished reading the program, and were ready to visit the Ladies' Fair, and the Wheatland School exhibit; to cast our ballots in the straw vote for president of the United States; to examine the old plows and the new tractors, washing machines, and television sets.

As we walked, we continued to look for Illinois natives—without success.

Later we drove off, still searching, down the straight quarter-section road.

Suddenly I caught a signal from the natives—a waving signal.

"Oh! there they *are!*" I shouted, pushing hard on imaginary brakes.

Europe in the churchyard

Illinois natives on the slope

Europe in the plowland

"Where?" probably the size of my shout had left my family half-expecting something dramatic like buffaloes, or Indians.

But the natives I had seen had found a hiding place that the Indians and buffaloes could not use. They were not in the green strip along the road. That autumn greenness belongs to European plants, adjusted to a lingering autumn that oozes halfheartedly into winter. Nor were my natives in the fields beyond the fence. That hybrid corn of Mexican and Central American ancestry was too tall, too dun, too stiff, to be a native.

But there in the fence row They stood!

Their sanctuary was only a foot wide. But it was a quarter-section long. They were safe because the road worker's mower does not reach there; and the farmer does not plow there.

We got out, and crossed the green strip of Europe, to the fence row; the purple claws of the turkey-foot grass waved above our heads, just as they waved above the heads of the first Spaniards, the first Frenchmen, the first trappers, the first oxen drawing the first covered wagons on the long journey from the East.

Nor was the big bluestem entirely bereft of its ancient companions. As we walked the fence rows, we found colonies of switch grass and cord grass, little bluestem and wild rye.

At first we could not find the other contemporary that belonged with these—the Indian grass. But, finally, we located it, too, in a different sort of sanctuary, the slope behind the fence of a little German-Lutheran churchyard.

Above the slope, in the shorn precision of the burial plot, there were plant foreigners. Below the slope, on the plowed land, there were foreigners, too. But the steep slope in between could be neither plowed nor mowed, and there a few bunches of Indian grass stood tall. They were hobnobbing, these outcasts from the prairie, with that outcast from gardens, the bouncing Bet, or lady-by-the-gate.

The sun set, then, on natives and foreigners alike, and we drove home, talking about fences.

At home we turned at once to the old books to see what we could find about the coming of fences to the prairie—contemporary comments such as we had been reading in the Plowing Match program.

The first reference that we unearthed overlapped the period of time covered by the program. In 1885 a State Law was passed, in an attempt to keep swine and cattle from running at large within the corporate limits of local communities. "Although a woman had been gored in the village streets, Naperville had paid little attention to the law . . . the less affluent citizens . . . contended that the streets were the poor man's pasture."

Naperville is our town.

Rufus Blanchard, writing of this area in 1882(7), told of the wide-ranging cattle on the prairie. "The writer once knew one of

Big bluestem,
turkey-foot grass,
Andropogon Gerardi

them [referring to a cow owner] to move six or eight miles and build a new cabin at the spot because his cow had chosen her range there."

We were fortunate to come across a little paper-bound booklet published in 1857(10), with a cover showing six oxen pulling a plow, and with this title:

The
ILLINOIS
CENTRAL RAILROAD COMPANY
offers for sale
Over 1,500,000 Acres
Selected
FARMING AND WOOD
LANDS
in tracts of Forty Acres and Upward
To Suit Purchasers
On Long Credit and At Low Rates of Interest
Situated
On each Side of Their Railroad, Extending All The Way
From the Extreme North to the South of
THE STATE OF ILLINOIS

On the subject of *Fencing* this booklet told the settler,

> An abundant supply of lumber, or timber for building or fencing, can be easily procured, but the Osage Orange plant has been extensively introduced, and is rapidly supplanting all other kinds of fencing. Being at the same time more permanent and more secure than any other, and highly ornamental, it must soon be universally employed. It can be raised by contract at from fifty to seventy-five cents per rod, parties making a business of preparing the ground, setting out the plants, and cultivating and trimming them until a perfect hedge is produced for the settler. For this, one third of the contract money is paid out upon the setting of the plants, and the balance when the fence is completed, without interest.

Those were the Osage oranges that have been so conspicuous in our northern Illinois scene as their brilliant orange roots have been grubbed out of the black soil that proved too valuable for them, after barbed wire came.

31

There are still left a few short remnants of Osage-orange hedge. But of the fence that preceded it, there is no trace.

B. G. Roots wrote, on December 27th, 1855, in a letter published in that same Illinois Central pamphlet:

> Fencing is the hardest work which a settler here has to perform. Good white oak rails, laid up in fence, are worth from 2 dollars to 3 dollars per hundred. To lessen the cost of fencing it is desirable for several friends to settle together, so that the land may at first be enclosed in one common field.

The angles of a rail fence made plenty of havens for prairie natives. In an account of an 1846 wolf hunt, not far from the Plowing Match site, we found a reference(16) to another kind of fence:

> The new settlers had commenced fencing their lands, and at several places the party had been obliged to dismount and remove the obstruction, but here they found a ditch fence.

The ditches and the mounds beside them have long ago been leveled.

"Were fences the first of the straight lines, and the right angles, on the face of the prairie?" wondered one of the family. "It is hard to visualize Wheatland township without that network of power lines, and roads, and fences—and furrows."

"Probably the furrows were the first straight lines," suggested another, and we turned back again to the old books, to see what contemporary writers had had to say about the first furrows on the face of the prairie.

At once we learned that settlers did not speak of "plowing" when they made those first furrows. They spoke of "breaking the prairie."

C. G. Taylor wrote, in 1856, from Rock Island, Illinois, in that same little Illinois Central pamphlet(10):

> The breaking of prairie is mostly done in May or June, though it can be carried on at any season when the frost is out of the ground. Many farmers use the heavy breaking plough, cutting a furrow from eighteen to twenty-six inches wide, and about three inches deep, requiring a force of from three to six yoke of oxen: of late, however, so many improvements have been made in the

form and draught of ploughs, that the prairie can be readily broken, at the rate of one and a quarter to one and a half acres per day, with a single pair of horses.

Sod corn, if planted in the month of May, and followed by favorable weather, viz. warm and dry, will yield from twenty to fifty bushels per acre. The planting is done by sticking an axe or spade between the layers of sod, and after dropping the corn, applying the heel of the boot freely. Only a small portion of prairie is yet broken.

Mr. James Phillips wrote, from Washington County, Illinois, in 1855(10):

All we have to do is to turn down the sod with a plough, at the rate of two or three acres a day, stick in the corn with an axe, and come out in Fall for the crop.

Prairie plow

C. B. Johnson, M.D., in memories of his childhood in "Illinois in the Fifties,"(13) recalled that:

Six yoke of oxen opened a furrow 2 feet or more in width, and the ox-driver carried a long whip of twisted raw-hide, which he was fond of flourishing with a sharp retort.

We found numerous references to breaking the prairie. They all agreed that the prairie sod was *deep* and *tough*, and that the prairie was rich and productive when the sod had been broken through.

That deep sod must have been broken occasionally before the oxen came. Gophers must have broken it, and perhaps an occasional woodchuck. Sometimes Nature must have taken advantage of such breaks. I believe that certain wide-spreading oaks that I pass every day, standing alone in a field, a stone's throw beyond the forest margin, may have got their start in gopher holes. Such a break in the sod would have made it possible for the new root thrusting downward out of the acorn to reach soil in the first season; whereas other acorns could not put out, in a single season, enough growth to penetrate to soil.

We can only speculate on the beginnings of those lone oaks, but we have records that men took advantage of gopher holes.

In 1820, Schoolcraft wrote(11):

> . . . the white hunters of Missouri and Arkansas frequently avail themselves of the labours of the gopher by planting corn upon the prairies that have been thus mellowed.

The Indians must have punctured the prairie, if they did not actually break it, for Tonti, companion of La Salle, wrote(4), in 1686, of an experience on the shore of Lake Michigan, soon after leaving the Chicago River:

> They lived on acorns and garlic found under the snow in the Pottowatamie village which they reached only to find it deserted. By good fortune they discovered a quantity of frozen squash and a little Indian corn and roasted it for food.

"Those men who broke the prairie," one of us wondered, remembering the wind, and the sun, "where did they live?"

"In the woods," the rest of us answered unhesitatingly, with knowledge gained from the many references we had come across, while reading about the breaking of the prairie.

We looked up those references again, and others.

In a small book compiled by the board of supervisors of Dupage County, in 1877(8), we read:

> After the close of the Blackhawk War the tide of emigration again turned to Illinois. . . . The first settlers selected, of course, the best locations, which were adjacent to timber. Scarcely any were to be found upon the prairie prior to 1837. All the

timber land was claimed before 1835, but some of the prairie land in our county, which at that day was considered almost worthless on account of its being inconvenient to timber, was never claimed by the squatters.

The Big Woods Claim Protection Society, in 1836(6), began its resolutions thus:

> Be it remembered, that we, the undersigned, inhabitants of the east side of the Big Woods, and its vicinity, have settled on lands belonging to the United States, and who have severally made their respective claims, including timber and prairie.

The old books referred constantly to "groves," and we noticed that most of the first settlements were called after them, Downer's Grove, Walker's Grove, Holderman's Grove, Babcock's Grove, and others.

An early account of French explorers(4) told that they

> likened the Illinois River to the Seine at Paris, . . . its bordering hills covered with fine trees, . . . they climbed to behold from their summits the prairies extending further than the eye could reach studded at regular intervals with groves seemingly planted in regular order.

Tonti, in his memoirs of 1684(4), said:

> . . . it is for the most part a great plain adorned with clusters of trees.

During the Black Hawk War, some ten to twenty miles west of the Plowing Match area(9):

> Major Stillman was permitted to make a tour of inspection up the river. . . . They continued their march to a small stream, where, on the 14th of May, 1832, a little before sundown, they dismounted in order to encamp for the night. Their encampment was judiciously selected in a beautiful oak grove, destitute of underbrush.

When oaks stand well spaced, "destitute of underbrush," and making an inviting camp site, those oaks are, in northern Illinois, almost inevitably bur oaks.

On a bright winter morning of January, 1834, a man named Charles Fenno Hoffman, according to his own account(14), set out on a trip from Chicago to St. Louis, by stagecoach, "in a handsome four-horse coach." The coach was given up for a sled with hay in the bottom, at Lawton's Grove. And night brought them to "Walker's Grove, which then consisted of two or three log huts, sheltered from the north wind under an island of tall timber."

The bur oak trunks

buffalo saw
them through
big bluestem

Indians saw them
between buffalo skins

pioneers saw them
through small windows

today people see them
through picture windows

Since Walker's Grove lies, or lay, just south of the present town of Plainfield, nearest town to the Plowing Match, we made a trip over there to see it.

A typical "prairie grove" we saw, with its great bur oaks standing well spaced.

Ranch houses are coming in under those massive branches now. And people look out through picture windows at the furrowed trunks. Pioneers saw such bur oak trunks, through much smaller apertures; Indians saw them between flapping buffalo skins, and buffalo saw them through tall turkey-foot grass.

We felt the thick bark and the corky twigs of the old bur oaks, and understood how this oak, rather than the red oak, or the white oak, could have withstood the Indian fires that swept the prairies and licked at the margin of the forest. It was easy to believe that the cambium (tissue-forming) layer would not have been so easily cooked under that corky insulation, as would the cambium of the thinner-barked trees.

The fires continually wiped out the thin-skinned underbrush, and so the prairie groves became a savannah type of forest, with a grassy floor.

"Do we know, for sure, about these Indian fires," came the question, "or do we simply assume their existence because of the evidence?"

Each of us instantly remembered some reference that had turned up in the old book while we were hunting material on prairie groves, or on "breaking the prairie," or on fences. We hunted up those references, and found many others as well. And incidentally, we learned that three things went together. When we found a record of fire, we found at the same time, a record of Indians and of buffaloes.

In 1834, according to an account published in 1857(6), Indian fires were still to be expected in the Chicago area.

> . . . the first attempt at actual farming of which the writer has any account, was in the fall of 1834. Mason Smith and Hezekiah Duncklee cut and stacked a few tons of hay near Salt Creek, to keep a small pony—which they had brought all the way from Detroit. Their stack was completed after several hard days' labor, and they were advised to burn the grass for several rods around it in order to protect it from the annual fires set by the Indians.

In 1823, an English farmer, making a tour of the United States, to see the "prospects for British emigrants" was rather depressed by the fires. He, William Faux, wrote(5):

The season called Indian summer, which here commences in October, by a dark blue hazy atmosphere, is caused by millions of acres for thousands of miles around, being in a wide-spreading, flaming, blazing, smoking fire, rising up through wood and prairie, hill and dale, to the tops of low shrubs and high trees, which are kindled by the coarse, thick, long prairie grass— darkening the air, heavens, and earth, filling the whole horizon with yellow, palpable, tangible smoke, ashes and vapour, which affect the eyes of man and beast, and obscure the sun, moon, and stars, for many days, or until the winter rains descend to quench the fire and purge the thick, ropey air, which is seen, tasted, handled, and felt.

On the following day, near Princeton, Indiana, he wrote,

. . . we rode all day through fire and thick smoke, which met in pillar-like arches across the road, and compelled us to wait a while or turn aside.

A few days later, near Harmony, he wrote:

The everlasting sound of falling trees, which, being undermined by fires, are falling around almost every hour, night and day, produces a sound loud and jarring as the discharge of ordnance.

In 1820, Schoolcraft(11) described the use of fire:

. . . but on the upper Mississippi, where they are destitute of horses they make amends for this deficiency by several ingenious stratagems. One of the most common of these is the method of hunting with fire. For this purpose a great number of hunters dispose themselves around a large prairie where herds of buffalo happen to be feeding, and setting fire to the grass, encompass them on all sides. The buffalo, having great fear of fire, retire toward the center of the prairie as they see it approach, and here being pressed together in great numbers, many are trampled underfoot, and the Indians rushing in with their arrows and musketry, slaughter immense numbers in a short period. It is asserted that a thousand animals have been killed by this strata-gem in one day.

In 1682, La Salle(4) saw the Indians using fire in this way, not far south of the Plowing Match region,

When they emerged from the desolate region of the Kankakee marshes, they found great open plains covered with tall dry grass; and they knew that they had at last reached the land of the Illinois, the prairie country of which they had heard so much. Their expectations of game were disappointed, for the autumnal fires, lit by the natives while hunting, had driven away the buffalo.

In a journey of more than 60 leagues they shot only two lean deer, some swans, and two wild geese, a meager support for so large a party. Two-thirds of the men, dissatisfied from lack of food, planned to desert and join the Indians, whom they saw now and then in the distance hovering about the burning prairies, but LaSalle divined and frustrated the scheme. When their need was sorest, however, they found an enormous buffalo mired on the bank of the river. Twelve men with difficulty dragged the huge creature to the solid ground with their strongest rope, and its flesh furnished abundant supplies.

Such records kept by explorers and early settlers, leave little doubt about the existence of prairie fires where there were Indians and buffaloes.

The buffalo might have had a close connection with the Wheatland Plowing Match, if the Marquis de Galissonière, governorgeneral of Canada, had had his way. In 1750 he wrote(27) to the King of France, urging that "the little colony of the Illinois be not left to perish," and described the country as open and ready for the plough, and traversed by an innumerable multitude of buffaloes, "and these animals are covered with a species of wool, sufficiently fine to be employed in various manufactures." He suggested that "the buffalo, if caught and attached to the plough, would move it at a speed superior to that of the domestic ox."

As we searched for references to these various aspects of the prairie we came across two comments that were of interest chiefly because of the well-known men who wrote them. The more recent comment(8) was by Monroe, written to Thomas Jefferson, in 1786, concerning the Northwest Territory.

A great part of the territory is miserably poor, especially that near Lakes Michigan and Erie, and that upon the Mississippi and Illinois consists of extensive plains which have not had, from appearances, and will not have, a single bush on them for ages. The districts, therefore, within which these fall, will never contain a sufficient number of inhabitants to entitle them to membership in the confederacy.

The other comment(4), the very first account of this region, was written by Father Marquette, in 1684. He was following the Illinois River when he wrote:

> . . . they had seen nothing like this river, for the fertility of the land, its prairies, woods, wild cattle, stag, deer, wildcats, bustards, swans, ducks, parrots, and even beaver, and its many little lakes and rivers.

With this account by Father Marquette, our early human records relating to the story of the prairies were exhausted.

To continue our unravelling of the past, we turned, for a picture of the prairie that met the eyes of explorers and pioneers, to plants of undisturbed fence rows, undisturbed sections of old cemeteries, certain railroad rights of way, and whatever other pieces of northern Illinois prairie survived, unplowed, ungrazed.

In such sites, most omnipresent of all plants is big bluestem, thriving best on places that are neither dry nor wet. Its most probable companion is Indian grass, *Sorghastrum nutans*.

In the fence row near the Plowing Match, these two grasses were not accompanied by prairie flowers. But that fence row has not, for a long time, been subjected to fire. Prairie areas subjected to occasional burning have shown a tendency to form a more rich mixture of many species of prairie flowers—probably because the thick accumulation of matted undecayed vegetation, "prairie duff," favors grasses.

Big bluestem and Indian grass are usually a part of a rich mixture composed of New Jersey tea, blazing star, flowering spurge, puccoon, compass plant or rosin weed, blue-eyed grass, and stiff goldenrod, rattlesnake master, smooth aster, and white false indigo.

On drier, usually higher, areas within our surviving remnants of prairie, the little bluestem (*Andropogon scoparius*) is the dominating plant. Its most probable associates are leadplant, purple prairie clover, the goldenrod sometimes called "hill goldenrod" or "dyers-weed goldenrod," and daisy fleabane.

On moister, usually lower, places the principal grass is cord grass (*Spartina pectinata*), associating with Canada anemone, closed gentian, tall meadow rue, Sullivant's milkweed, wild strawberry, saw-toothed sunflower, black-eyed Susan, prairie dock, and Culver's root.

Whether the prairie is dry or wet or medium, it produces each growing season three successive layers of flowering, each one higher than the preceding one(19). As the summer progresses there is an ever-increasing feel of denim and calico and burlap in the foliage; a crescendo of the sounds of corduroy, tent-flaps, sails, as one walks through the prairie; a growing pungency; and a multiplying of the flower forms that wear the Composite-family pattern, an image of the sun.

The three types of prairie—dry, wet, and medium—are all represented in fence rows within a three-mile radius of the plowing-match site. The lowest, wettest areas contain not only cord grass, but cord grass in association with sedges and smartweed. At one time it is probable that cord grass was dominant over much of this area. The soil must have become gradually drier through the years, as a result of alluvial deposits; through the development of the drainage pattern in this area where glacial drift had destroyed or plugged old patterns; and through the construction of drainage ditches and the tiling of the fields. As the drying progressed the cord-grass areas were taken over by big bluestem and its associates.

The presence of a few sedges in some cord-grass areas suggests the possibility of a preceding stage, dominated by cattails. The geological map of this area shows a bay of the post-glacial Lake Waubonsee, covering much of the plowing-match vicinity. Along the shallow margins of that bay, the sedge and cord-grass stage may have been preceded by the other stages of a filling lake, as discussed in the chapter "Coming Ashore."

While the cord-grass areas are reminiscent of a post-glacial body of water, little bluestem areas on the drier ridges suggest the great ice-sheet itself, depositing those ridges.

But the story of the prairie reaches back even farther than to the time of the glacier. The record in rocks tells of prairie before the cold interlude of invaders from the north, as well as afterward —prairie in the high places, prairie in the low places, prairie in the medium places.

But why did these low places, these high places, these medium places, become prairie?

Why not forest?

With that question we step out onto a battleground, an old scarred battleground of midwestern botanists, where many a shiny theory has met defeat, and where raw material has been assembled for many a thesis offered toward a Master's degree, or Doctor's degree. (Most of the arguments in the following controversy are discussed by Transeau, in Number 1 of the references at the end of this chapter.)

Men have said, in essence:

> It is a matter of *rainfall*. More rainfall makes forest; less rainfall makes prairie.

Others have answered:

> Under the same annual rainfall, some regions produce forest, others produce prairie.

Men have said:

> The reason prairies are found, where, on the basis of rainfall, forests might be expected, is that *the soil is too fine*. Forest trees need a coarse, loose soil.

Others have answered:

> Trees grow anywhere in Illinois where they are planted, and there are prairies on many textures of soil.

Men have said:

> It is a matter of *soil constituents*.

42

Others have answered:

Prairie remnants are found on hilltops, and in marsh land, on cliff edges, and in bogs, on sandstone, outcrops, and on limestone, on sand dunes, and in ponds.

Men have said:

Prairies mark the sites of filled lakes, or of a continuous chain of *water drainage.*

Others have pointed out:

Some prairies are high, some are low; some are well drained, some are poorly drained.

Men have said:

Prairies inhabit areas that are *geologically young.*

Others have answered:

There are younger regions that are covered with forest.

Men have said:

The prairie is a deciduous forest temporarily without trees, the trees having been eliminated by hardships that have long ago ceased to exist. The natural forest would have returned if man had not kept the prairie open by farming.

Others have answered:

It is true that forests preceded prairies in this part of the country (certainly bog pollen records seem to indicate such a past), but that was thousands of years ago, before the uplift of the western mountains robbed the west winds of their moisture. Fossils from the Late Tertiary period show an abundance of dryland grasses already inhabiting the plains.

Then men have said, pointing to the trees that are now growing on prairie soil, especially on the wet prairie:

If *they grow there now,* it is to be supposed that they might have grown there formerly.

But others have said, pointing to the extensive system of drainage ditches, and the thousands of miles of tile:

> Most of the rainfall is run off into the rivers now, so that the water table is seldom raised, and so that the farmers have had three times to deepen their wells. The wet prairie is not so wet as it was formerly.

Men have said:

> This part of the country has seesawed back and forth *between prairie and forest.* When there has been a dry period, the prairie has pushed the forest back; when there has been a wet period, the forest has pushed the prairie back.

Others have answered:

> That is, in part, true, but only in small part. There were thousands of oaks that died in the intense drought of 1914-1915. But the typical prairie earths, that are deep as far east as central Ohio, speak of a long, continuous prairie tenancy.

Many men have said:

> *Indian fires* made the prairie.

Others have answered:

> It has been observed that the result of fires in forest is scrub forest; the result of fires in prairie is maintaining the prairie. It has never been observed that a fire made a prairie.

> And there is no conclusive difference between the vegetation on the west bank of our larger streams, as compared with the vegetation on the east bank. In our prevailing westerlies, a large river would have given enough protection to the east bank, to have kept more forest remnants there, if Indians made prairie out of forest.

Men have said:

> The Indians may not have made prairie out of forest, but, after some extremes of Nature made the prairie, the Indians maintained it by fire—else it would long ago have returned to the original forest.

44

Others have answered:

When the glacier receded, the northern vegetation that had moved south before the glacier, left behind many relict communities, of pine, and tamarack, and hemlock, in states of the Midwest, especially in bogs; but not a single relict community was left behind on the Prairie Peninsula, though there were plenty of depressions that might have held bogs. Evidently, then, trees did not thrive here, even without the influence of Indians or fires.

Men have said:

It is a matter of competition, and grasses got there first. Whenever prairie soil is disturbed, as along ditches, cottonwoods abound. During our present climate the prairies east of the Mississippi delay invasion by forest only by the nature of their prairie soil.

Others have answered:

In some places where prairie land has been plowed and subseqently abandoned, it has gone back to prairie; not in all places—there are many exceptions in Iowa, for example, especially in valleys, and on stream margins. The prairie shows more and more stability against invasion by forest the further west it lies.

Bohumil Shimek, in "Papers on the Prairie"(23) says, "The breaking of the prairie turf is sufficient to cause most of the prairie plants to disappear from the broken surface, but there is abundant evidence to show that it requires continued cultivation to keep them out. Their return is rather slow and is preceded by a transitional mixture of species, but it is quite certain, provided man does not interfere." He concludes a study of certain tracts with this statement: "The views that prairie will disappear for all time if broken, and that, with cessation of prairie fires, the forest will take possession of the prairie, are untenable in the light of these and similar prairie tracts."

Homer Sampson(2) recounts the story of a strip of farm land on his father's farm near Wheeler, Illinois. A railroad right of way that had been fifty feet wide was, in 1897, made eighty feet wide by the addition of a fifteen foot strip on each side. To this strip came back the big bluestem prairie.

45

Today some men are saying:

> The outstanding factor in making prairie on the Prairie Peninsula, east of the Mississippi extension of the prairie, is the ratio between evaporation and rainfall.

> Certainly the relative humidity is lower on the Prairie Peninsula than it is to the north and to the south of this area that reaches, like a hand with many long fingers, eastward from the Iowa prairie. Occasionally that ratio is so extreme as to make a severe summer drought. Those summer droughts have been a potent factor in shaping the prairie.

To this theory of relative humidity and drought, some others have answered:

> Yes, it is ever demonstrated that the extremes determine what is to be the native vegetation. The averages are not nearly so important as the extremes. It is plain that prairie grasses can wait. They can seize the good years, and lie low through the bad ones, putting out a minimum of growth.

> And the different kinds of grasses can take turns at prosperity. The kind of grass that the shoe fits can put it on. Some wet years it fits the cord grass. Some dry years it fits the little bluestem.

> Grasslands can endure fire, whether made by man or lightning or meteor, because the grasses can rise again from their roots. And they can shade out a forest seedling, if one should succeed in putting down a root long enough to pierce the sod.

A prairie, then, is shaped by many forces: by fire, water and wind, by Indians and buffaloes; most of all, by the ratio between rainfall and evaporation; and by occasional periods of extreme drought.

A prairie is vanquished by two forces: domestic grazing animals and the plow.

Cows ate the tall grasses off too close to the ground. Lower grasses could endure that close cropping. Consequently the tall prairie grasses were gradually replaced.

If the prairie was dry, the turkey foot was replaced by bluegrass, from Eurasia. If switch grass was the dominant grass, it, too, was replaced by bluegrass.

If the prairie was wetter, with cord grass dominant, or switch grass, they were replaced by redtop, from Eurasia.

Both of these replacements form a low turf.

We drove out to the plowing-match site again, in October—not directly, but in a wide arc, because we wanted to enjoy the fall color in the fence-row strips of prairie.

The little bluestem was exquisite with turquoise and garnet and chartreuse; and the big bluestem waved its turkeyfeet of deep purple high against the October sky, past the warm russet of the Indian grass.

In one long strip, a farmer was at work, taking down his fence.

"Why?" we asked.

"Easier to work it without fences," he answered. "If I ever want to turn stock onto this field, it's easy to string up an electric fence."

That will be the end of that colorful rectangle of prairie, one foot wide, one-half mile long, and eight feet deep.

We picked a few purple turkeyfeet to take home. They make pleasant bookmarks in the old books.

REFERENCES

1. "The Prairie Peninsula" by Edgar Nelson Transeau. *Ecology* **16** (July, 1935), 423-437.
2. *An Ecological Survey of the Prairie Vegetation of Illinois* by Homer

Sampson (Illinois Natural History Survey 13). State of Illinois, Urbana, 1921.

3. "The Vegetational History of the Middle West" by H. A. Gleason. *Annals of the Association of American Geographers* 12 (1922), 39-85.

4. *Découvertes et établissements des Français den l'ouest et dan le sud de l'Amérique septentrionale (1614-1698)* by Pierre Margy. Maisonneuve et Cie., Paris, 1879.

5. *Indiana as Seen by Early Travelers; A Collection of Reprints from Books of Travel, Letters, and Diaries Prior to 1830,* edited by Harlow Lindley. Indiana Historical Commission, Indianapolis, Indiana, 1916.

6. *History of Du Page County, Illinois,* by C. W. Richmond and H. F. Vallette. Steam presses of Scripps, Bross and Spears, Chicago, 1857.

7. *History of Du Page County, Illinois,* by Rufus Blanchard. O. L. Baskin and Company, Chicago, 1882.

8. *The Settlement of Illinois 1778–1830* by Arthur Clinton Boggess. Chicago Historical Society, Chicago, 1908.

9. *History of Illinois* by Henry Brown. J. Winchester, New York, 1844.

10. [The Illinois Central Railroad Offer for Sale of Selected Farm and Wood Lands in Illinois] Rand and Avery, Boston, 1857.

11. *Narrative Journal of Travels Through the Northwestern Regions of the United States; Extending from Detroit Through the Great Chain of American Lakes, to the Sources of the Mississippi River. Performed as a Member of the Expedition under Governor Cass. In the year 1820,* by Henry Rowe Schoolcraft. E. and E. Hosford, Albany, 1821.

12. *Travels in the Central Portions of the Mississippi Valley; Comprising Observations on Its Mineral Geography, Internal Resources, and Aboriginal Population,* by Henry Rowe Schoolcraft. Collins and Hannay, New York, 1825.

13. *Illinois in the Fifties: or, A Decade of Development 1851–1860,* by Charles B. Johnson. Flanigan-Pearson Company, Champaign, Illinois, 1918.

14. *Chicago's Highways, Old and New,* by Milo Milton Quaife. D. F. Keller and Company, Chicago, 1923.

15. "The Invasion of a Planted Prairie Grove" by Raymond J. Pool. *Proceedings of the Society of American Foresters* 10 (January, 1915), Number 1.

16. *The North American Buffalo; a Critical Study of the Species in Its Wild State,* by Frank Gilbert Roe. University of Toronto Press, Toronto, 1951.

17. "The Indian as an Ecological Factor in the Northeastern Forest" by Gordon M. Day. *Ecology* 34 (April, 1953), 329-436.
18. *Eight Months in Illinois, with Information to Emigrants,* by William Oliver. Walter M. Hill, Chicago, 1924 (originally published at Newcastle upon Tyne, 1843).
19. *The North American Prairie* by J. E. Weaver. Johnsen Publishing Company, Lincoln, Nebraska, 1954.
20. *Horses: The Story of the Horse Family in the Modern World and Through Sixty Million Years of History,* by George Gaylord Simpson. Oxford, New York, 1951.
21. *Plants, Man and Life,* by Edgar Anderson. Little, Brown, Boston, 1952.
22. "Soil and Proteins" by William A. Albrecht. *The Land* 7 (1948), Number 2.
23. *Papers on the Prairie* by Bohumil Shimek. Studies in Natural History 11, Number 5, University of Iowa, Iowa City, 1925.
24. "Structure of Prairie Vegetation" by T. L. Steiger. *Ecology* 11 (January, 1930), 170-217.
25. "A Prairie Continuum in Wisconsin" by J. T. Curtis. *Ecology* 36 (October, 1955), 588.
26. "De Gannes Memoir." Illinois Historical Collections, Volume 23 (French Series, Volume 1, page 302), Illinois State Historical Library, Springfield.
27. *Chapters from Illinois History* by Edward G. Mason. H. S. Stone and Company, Chicago, 1901.

3.

COMING ASHORE

or

As Lake Changes to Land

How many times had my canoe slid to shore with that identical sequence of sounds!

But I had not been conscious of the sequence, until one windless evening when I rested the paddle to wonder what had suddenly made me think of Denmark. What feature of a starlit Wisconsin lake had summoned up the memory of Fru Gormsen hurrying to the window to peer into the narrow strip of mirror fastened to the outside of the window frame? It wasn't her checking on passersby that was memorable. Every house along that cobblestoned street had a similar mirror for that purpose, outside the lace curtains. It was what she had said, even before she looked, breathing it softly because the windows were open:

"Americans!"

"But how did you know?" we asked when they had passed.

"Silk petticoats," she explained. "I heard silk petticoats." (That was in 1920.)

Silk petticoats! They must have been the link between the canoe and the memory. The canoe was sliding across lily pads with a silken sound.

But hardly had I realized the sound before it was succeeded by a different one. The bow was separating cattails with a subdued rustling, like that of a popcorn sack at the movies.

The cattail rasp seemed so inevitable after the silken sliding over the lily pads, so obviously one of a series of sounds, that I asked myself what had preceded the sliding.

Was it the dip and drip of the paddle in open water? Was the sequence, *drip, slide, rustle?*

No, there was something missing in that sequence. Something between the *drip* and the *slide.*

There was an interval filled with a sort of tangled dripping, the stretch between open water and waterlilies—that stretch where submerged pondweeds enmesh the paddle and change the clean drip to a muffled spatter.

The sequence was: *drip, spatter, slide, rustle.*

I pushed off again, and went to test this sequence at another landing place—and another. The darkness seemed to help me hear the changes in sound, as keel and paddle stirred the surface of the lonely lake. *Drip, spatter, slide, rustle.*

But next day I went out to use eyes as well as ears on the situations that had shaped those sounds. I took along a fish pole.

Out in the area of clean *drip* the water was dark and clear. It looked devoid of life, but a microscope would reveal myriads of tiny transparent plants and animals. I knew the coldness of that deep water, because we used to dive into it from the seat of a row boat. The boys would bring up what they could in their hands. It was not much; it was, for the most part, sand and gravel, with a little trace of blackness, probably the residue of the dead bodies of microscopic floating life, and of material washed out toward the center from the margin of the lake. Once, long ago, immediately after the glacial ice had melted, the entire bottom of the lake must have been clean and free of all life. Then began the long slow process of filling in, the first stage being the appearance of microscopic forms of plant and animal life.

In addition to the microscopic life of that area of open clear water, there were a few algae floating free. I scooped up a handful of the filmy threads.

This free-floating life below the surface of the water seems to have a minimum of problems of protection, of survival, of food supply. Thin, permeable membranes, bathed continuously in an everlasting supply of nourishment, need no mechanical tissues for standing against the wind, no insulation against the thirsty sun, no roots for anchorage or food intake. And when winter comes, they need only sink to the bottom and await the warmth of spring. There is no need for floral structures fitted to bees or moths or wind or

FIRST STAGE in a small filling lake
free-floating microscopic plants and animals; and algae

cross section of margin

bird's-eye view

water, even, for reproduction is accomplished by one body's splitting into two, or by a simple emptying of one cell into another, all under the water.

I paddled out of the *drip* area into the *spatter* area. Now I could look down into a rich growth of plants and see perch and bluegills swimming among them. With the long fish pole I poked down to learn the depth of the water. In most of the area it measured from ten to five feet.

After I had measured in a few places the fish pole became encrusted with the gritty scum which covered the surface of the water. Actually, this scum consisted of flowers, millions of them—the pollen-bearing flowers of the eel grass, *Vallisneria*. These had been released from a short stalk, far below on the floor of the lake, and sent bobbing to the surface. Most of them were drifting uselessly about, but here and there I saw some flowers that were fulfilling their destiny.

These flowers had been drawn into tiny dimples in the surface film—dimples made by the female, or pistillate flowers. The female flowers were not nearly so numerous as the male ones, nor were they

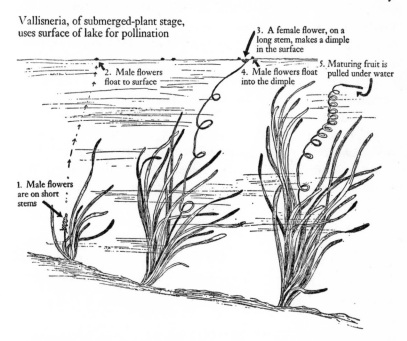

Vallisneria, of submerged-plant stage, uses surface of lake for pollination

3. A female flower, on a long stem, makes a dimple in the surface

5. Maturing fruit is pulled under water

2. Male flowers float to surface

4. Male flowers float into the dimple

1. Male flowers are on short stems

floating free. Each one was attached to a long corkscrew stem. One that I managed to pull up into the canoe was twelve feet long, flexible, gummy.

Pollen-bearing flowers that floated into a dimple were sure to rub some pollen against the stigma of the pistillate flower. Around the canoe I could see plenty of pistillate flowers that gave evidence of having been successfully pollinated. They had pulled in their lines. The long corkscrew stems had tightened up their coils and were pulling the plumping seed pods down into the water.

The waterweed called Elodea uses the surface of water for its pollinating agent in much the same way that the Vallisneria does. But, like most of these submerged plants, it does not depend on seeds for distribution, but reproduces readily from segments broken off from the parent plant. This ability of Elodea has made it a real pest in Europe. Robert Gathorne-Hardy, in his "Wild Flowers in Britain" (10), tells us that in "the early 1850's a piece of Elodea from the Oxford Botanical Gardens fell into the Cherwell. In 1853 it was seen in the Thames at Folly Bridge. Between 1866 and 1874 it had rendered parts of the Thames almost unnavigable."

Since there are only pistillate plants of Elodea in Europe, it is certain that this invasion has been by fragmentation, not by seeds.

I pulled up several kinds of submerged plants into the canoe: pondweeds, *Potamogeton;* hornwort, *Ceratophyllum;* white water crowfoot, *Ranunculus trichophyllus;* water milfoil, *Myriophyllum.* They were all swathed in algae. The spineless supine plants hung limp in my hands, as soon as there was no water to support them and give them form; and they broke apart easily at the joints. All that flaccid verdure, lying in a collapsed heap across the ribs of the canoe, was evidence of little need for mechanical tissue; of no need for protective structures. These thin-walled leaves are often, in submerged plants, quite as important in absorbing nutrients as are the roots.

The roots that I managed to pull up were unimpressive. As I lifted the mass from the floor to dump it over the side, it seemed to weigh less than might be expected. That was probably because of the big air chambers in the stems, a typical feature of submerged plants. Here and there jelly-like masses clung to the stems. In some of the masses I could see tiny spirals of snail forms developing.

Schools of little fish poured past. A tern dipped close beside me. I knew from experience that a leech was probably biding his time down there among the waterweeds, waiting his long wait for blood.

Except for the plants that were using the surface film as a pollinating agent, and for the snails that took a swallow of air down below with them, life in this zone was still shaped by a water medium, still submerged.

This stage of submerged life was gradually raising the level of the bottom, not only by the accumulation of partly decomposed plant and animal remains, but also, especially, by the slowing down of the currents, thus causing the deposit of inorganic material washed into the lake from surrounding shores.

Now the canoe was starting to slide over waterlily pads. No wonder their sound had been noticeably different in the night. Here

SECOND STAGE
submerged plants

cross section of margin

pondweeds
eelgrass
water milfoil
hornwort
Elodea

bird's-eye view

was a rigid waxed surface. The leaves that the canoe had passed over did not appear to be as wet as might be expected of leaves that had been pushed down under water. Keeping the surfaces dry above is important to these floating leaves. Unlike the submerged plants whose leaves, for the most part, have none of the minute openings called stomates, and unlike land plants, whose leaves usually have stomates on their under surfaces, the waterlily bears leaves with stomates on the upper surface. The upturned edges of the leaves, as well as the wax, help to keep the surface dry.

I poked the fish pole down again among the waterlily pads. Here it measured depths ranging from five to two feet. The stems had neither stiffness nor wax. They were stout, flexible hawsers, that allowed the leaves to float freely, rising and falling with changing

55

water depths. The flowers floated, too, on green sepals whose shape might have been the inspiration for the first canoe.

I picked a flower, and pulled it apart carefully, starting at the outside, and laying the individual parts in concentric circles on the floor of the canoe. (They had been growing in a similar concentric formation, but a more compact one.)

The outer parts wore a little white on their edges. The next whorl was less green and more white. Next were several bands of pure, gleaming white. Nearer the center, the white petals began narrowing and dwindling in size. Then there was one bearing a trace of yellow at its tip. The next petal had a bit more of the yellow. Each successive part showed more yellow, and dwindled further in size, until these were not petals that I was pulling off and laying down—they were stamens. But I could not lay my finger on any one place and say, "This is where petals stop and stamens begin."

This arrangement of flower parts suggests that a leafy stem, foreshortened, telescoped, might end up looking something like this. Reading in, from the outside toward the center, might be like reading a tabloid account of the development of a flower from a leafy stem —even to characteristic tabloid inaccuracies.

Looking down on the fluidity of that floral pattern of the waterlily, I was reminded of other flowers that show stamens that are half petal, or petals that are part sepal: delphiniums, peonies, roses, poppies, hollyhocks. Hybridizers, quick to recognize the possibilities of the unstable and, as yet, uncrystallized nature of such floral material, have encouraged the production of petals, at the expense of stamens. The wild rose of the field has become the many-petaled rose of the florist.

Such plasticity belongs to the primitive flowers—flowers from the lower branches of the floral family tree, from the living fossils; and consequently, flowers from the first pages of our systematic flower books.

In flowers from the uppermost branches of the floral family tree, flowers more recently arrived on the earth, the pattern is more rigid, more fixed. These present no such fertile field for hybridizers bent on doubling floral parts. Changes come hard to plants, or people, when their patterns are fixed, inflexible.

A beetle landed to inspect the dissected flower at my feet in the canoe. Then he took off for a growing one, beside the canoe. After he left, another beetle came, and another, then a fly, followed by a bee.

At first glance it looked as if these insects' visits could have no role in seed production, but inspection showed that the pistils were

THIRD STAGE
floating-leaved plants

not ready to receive pollen at the same time that the stamens in the same flowers were ready to give off pollen. This meant that these flowers must depend on insects to carry ripened pollen from one to another.

On the yellow pondlily growing nearby, the flower opened on its first day only wide enough to expose the receptive surface of its pistil; later it opened wide enough to expose the stamens that would furnish pollen for another partially opened flower.

I noticed a neat circular hole in a leaf of the yellow pondlily and pulled the leaf in to investigate. On the underside of the leaf, the hole was partly ringed about with a double row of white eggs, arranged radially. These were the eggs of *Donacia*, the leaf beetle. She had bitten the hole, and inserting her abdomen through it, had deposited the eggs there. It had probably been a *Donacia* that had gleamed with metallic bronze and green on the floor of the canoe for a moment when she came to inspect the parts of my waterlily.

Like the waterlily, she lives a life that uses both the lake and its surface, as well as the air above it. When those eggs hatch in about ten days, the little larvae will drop down into the water, but they will breathe air during their entire existence. They will attach themselves to the stout stem of a waterlily plant; this they will rasp with their spines, until they have made a hole. Into this hole each larva will push its head and thorax, and breathe the air that is in the air chambers of the stem—the same air that makes bubbles in the water when a waterlily stem is broken underwater. When the time approaches for the larvae to enter the second phase of their life cycle and to become pupae, each one builds a cocoon, silky and water-tight, that holds this pupa or resting stage, in a place where air is available. And when the adult emerges from the pupal case, its body, enmeshed in silk and buoyed up by a bubble of waterlily air, floats to the surface, ready to begin again a life in the air.

The donacia eggs were not the only things attached to the under-side of that leaf. There was a snail, and two small deposits of snail eggs in jelly, and a few elongated eggs, probably of the damsel fly. And in the shadow of another leaf a sunfish was hiding.

The waxy upper surface of these leaves had become familiar to me by moonlight and by flashlight, because we had come often in the canoe to turn our flashlight beams on the shining bubble of the throat of a swamp cricket frog or of a tree frog. These two, when filling our nights with the sound of clicking stones and sleigh bells, would invariably go right on with their songs even though we paddled close enough to touch them, and turned our lights full upon them. The green frog's banjo twang, and the bull-frog's "jug-o-rum" would pause briefly after we crept close, but they too would soon resume full strength. Amphibian voices, the first voices to be heard on the young earth when animals came ashore, belong in this zone in which plant and animal life has both submerged and emergent phases; and where the frog, beginning his life breathing water and ending it breathing air, is colored below like the water and above like a lily pad.

The floating-leaved plants altogether add considerable bulk to the lake margin, both of their own mass and by their catching of material washed in from the shore.

As I moved in from the *slide* sound of the waterlily leaves to the *rustle* of cattails, I used the fish pole again for locating the bottom in the muck of this emergent-plant zone.

At no place was the water more than two feet deep; in most of the cattail zone it was only six inches, or less.

Cattails, sedges, and bulrushes stood upright, sparse toward the waterlily zone, but densely crowded toward the shore. The leaves, reinforced against wind, sun, and decay, sounded and felt very different from the waxy saucers of the floating plants, the flaccid sponginess of the submerged plants.

The wind is important in the economy of the lake margin. Flowers of this zone depend on it for carrying their pollen. Here is no floating pollen-bearing flower such as the submerged Vallisneria sends bobbing to the surface; no knobby, heavy pollen sticky enough to cling to the hairy parts of insects, such as the waterlily produces. Instead, there is light, winged dust, suited to air travel, and prodigiously abundant, only a minute fraction of which is ever likely to arrive at a working destination. There is no insect appetite to guide this pollen, no chemical attraction, no dimple in the water film.

I examined a cattail. It was brown and thick. The upper part of the spike was shriveled, with all its pollen spent. A few weeks ago that upper part was golden, dusty, and thick. If struck, it would pour forth a cloud of pollen. The lower part of the spike was thinner then. You had to look with a hand lens to see the myriad stigmas held out like tongues. Those tongues must have caught their pollen, because the cattail was now swelling with ripening seeds.

Later in the season the wind will again become important to the cattails. That will be when their seeds are ripe and equipped with fluff for flight.

59

The erectness of the vegetation in this zone was being utilized by dragonflies and damsel flies. Above the water on cattails and rushes clung many ghostlike empty skins, split down the back. Those skins had contained fierce voracious creatures that crawled on the floor of the lake, seizing and eating anything smaller than themselves, and sometimes tackling living things a little larger. That was during the nymph stage of the dragonfly. Anyone who has put a few of these into an aquarium, and watched them eat up the other

FOURTH STAGE
emergent plants

cross section of margin

cattails
bulrushes
sedges

bird's-eye view

inhabitants, then start in on each other, knows how vicious they can appear. The winged creatures that emerge from those whitening skins merely shift the scene of their hunting to the air above.

The surface of the water among the cattails was alive with gyrating battalions of whirligig beetles, and with the water striders, skating on the surface film with each foot in a dimple of water.

The canoe grated slightly on the narrow strip of shore, where clam tracks and clams and the masonry shelters of caddis flies were abundant.

There was the crackle of a fallen willow twig as I stepped out.

Among the willow trees around the lake are a few elms, many silver maples and ashes. There are no oak seedlings among them. Not yet. The hills around the lake are covered with oaks, but those hills are moraines, and their story is one that begins with dryness, not wetness.

The bottomland trees that are now only a fringe around the shallower shores of the lake will some day step out farther onto the mucky bottoms where cattails have prepared the way for them.

Then the cattails will grow out on the decaying remains of water-lilies.

The waterlilies, in turn, will float new leaves where submerged plants, and materials they have enmeshed, have built up the bottom so that it is shallow enough for them to get a foothold.

The submerged plants will then invade areas that have become less deep as materials have been washed out from the shallower margin.

Presently the submerged plants from one shore will meet the submerged plants advancing from an opposite shore, and gradually the water will become too shallow even for them.

Then the waterlilies from one shore will meet those progressing from another, and presently the water will become too shallow for them also.

The cattails will be right behind them.

The willows will lead then in the advancing company of bottom-land trees. Eventually violets, Virginia bluebells, and wild ginger will bloom where the waterlily once floated. Orioles will nest where the tern dipped.

If the lake happens to be in the prairie region, the cattail stage will be succeeded by wet-land grasses, instead of willows.

In either case a canoe will be out of place.

This is the story of filling lakes, thousands of filling lakes.

Some lakes have different stories. Successions may be changed or modified, accelerated or slowed down, by such features as the nature of the substrata; the material of the surrounding slopes; the degree of slope of the shore, and the basin; altitude; latitude; or the development of the drainage pattern. There is a different story in an undrained, or poorly drained depression. This one is told in the chapter, History Book with Flexible Cover.

Sometimes man inserts himself into the sequence. He may raise water levels with dams. Then waterlilies may float again where violets and wild ginger have been for a time; and terns may dip again where the oriole has nested. Man may decide to halt the suc-

FIFTH STAGE
trees

bird's-eye view

cross section of margin

willows
silver maples

cessions artificially, and capture a desired stage, instead of allowing the natural course of events to proceed. He does this in cranberry bogs, for example, and in areas flooded to maintain the species that are pasture for waterfowl.

In the end, however much the intervening story may have been modified, events march inexorably toward a time when wheels may turn where the canoe once floated; and the surface may be stirred into a cloud of dust, where once it was stirred into the sounds of *"drip, spatter, slide, rustle."*

REFERENCES

1. *Animal Communities in Temperate America* by Victor Ernest Shelford. University of Chicago Press, Chicago, 1937.
2. *Clean Waters for New York State* by James G. Needham. Cornell Rural School Leaflet 13, Number 4, Dept. for Rural Education, Cornell University, Ithaca, N. Y.
3. *Field Book of Ponds and Streams* by Ann Haven Morgan. Putnam, New York, 1936.
4. *Field Book of Animals in Winter* by Ann Haven Morgan. Putnam, New York, 1939.
5. "Plant Succession of Long Pond, Long Island, New York," by Dorothy Parker. *Butler University Botanical Studies* 7 (April, 1945), 74-88.
6. "Plant Succession About Douglas Lake, Cheboygan County, Michigan," by Frank C. Gates. *Botanical Gazette* 82 (1926), 170-182.
7. "The Development of Vegetation in the English Lakes Considered in Relation to the General Evolution of Glacial Lake and Rock Basins" by W. H. Pearsall. *Proceedings of Royal Society, London* Series B 92 (1921), 259–284.
8. *Fishery Science* by George A. Rounsefell and W. Harry Everhart. Wiley, New York, 1953.
9. *The Life of Inland Waters* by James G. Needham and J. T. Lloyd. Comstock Publishing Company, Ithaca, N. Y., 1937.
10. *Wild Flowers in Britain* by Robert Gathorne-Hardy. B. T. Batsford, London, 1938.

4.

HISTORY BOOK WITH FLEXIBLE COVER
or
The Records in a Quaking Bog

"You're walking on a history book," said the professor. "It happens, you may notice, to have a flexible cover."

"And to be extremely absorbing," added the undergraduate, using both hands to pull his other foot out of the ooze.

That was my introduction to the Mineral Springs bog—to any bog.

A member of the class broke through the flexible cover that day, up to her waist, and had to lie down on the sphagnum moss and cranberries before we could pry her out. She never did retrieve her shoes, but that was because she had, unfortunately, taken the professor seriously, on the day before the field trip, when he answered our question of "What shall we wear?" by saying "Better wear pumps."

On a later ecology field trip to that same bog, one of the men students killed a rattlesnake there.

On a still later trip, my companion, a young nonbotanical advertising man, cut a walking stick and carried it all day; and I thought nothing of it until, the following week, he called me from the hospital where he lay, his eyes swollen shut with poison sumac.

On that first trip to the bog, we all sat for a while on the end of an old black oak sand dune among columbines and bird's-foot violets while some students put on boots against the water or gloves against the poison sumac; and some put on protection against the mosquitoes (it was citronella in those days); some told tales of teams of horses that had disappeared in bogs; and inevitably someone mentioned "The Slough of Despond."

Then we crossed the narrow old corduroy road, which is said to have once carried stagecoaches from Michigan City to Chicago.

We passed the fringe of sour gum trees and took a few steps down, down among the cinnamon ferns—textured acres of them.

Those three or four steps down from the road transported us magically from that bog in northern Indiana, to the woods of northern Wisconsin or northern Michigan. The trees around us were yellow birch, white pine, red maple, arborvitae. The shrubs were red-berried elder and winterberry (*Ilex verticillata*). On knolls about the tree roots we looked down upon a rich carpet of goldthread, wintergreen, bunchberry, starflower, Indian cucumber root, partridgeberry.

The two sides of the road seemed to have nothing in common, until we found, on a low branch above the cinnamon ferns, the hummingbird's nest with its two oblong eggs. That structure made a link. It was built of wool from the stipe of the cinnamon fern, and encrusted with lichens from the base of the yellow birch, and some of the food-energy for the building of it had doubtless come from the long nectar sacs of the wild columbine back there on the end of the dune where we had rested.

We swished ahead tenderly through the waist-high ferns to the point where their ranks thinned.

Then we found ourselves having to jump from the hummock at one tamarack's base to the hummock of the next tamarack. In between was black ooze. And in that ooze we found treasure—a clump of showy lady's slipper, *Cypripedium reginae.*

From this spot, the jumps between tamarack roots became longer and longer, and just as we would grab for an outstretched helpful-looking branch, someone would yell, "Look out! Poison sumac."

Between and beyond the poison sumac stretched open sunnier areas. Here we spent a joyful time jumping up and down to see the poison sumac several yards away jumping up and down with us, until the girl with the pumps broke through the surface. After she had been extricated, we still advanced gingerly, step by step, on the unstable mat. We were young and competitive, but we gave up among the cattails.

Idealized bog without bays, shallows, other complications.

FIRST STAGE
submerged plants on
lake floor near margin

From the yellow birches to the cattails we had been reading the story of a bog backward.

Now, as we stood, where our eyes could go farther though our feet could not, we began to consider the story of a bog chronologically. This story, from open water to forest, is written over and over again. It is the story of undrained depressions.

Many such undrained depressions are kettle holes in the moraine, places where masses of ice were left behind as the glacier receded. But the Mineral Springs bog lay in a long lagoon of an ancient beach.

Probably this long inland lake started filling with vegetation like any other lake, with submerged plants attached to the bottom near the edge of the lake.

Probably the second stage, too, was like the second stage of other filling lakes—a few waterlilies attached to the bottom and floating their leaves on the surface. These first two stages however had long ago disappeared from the Mineral Springs bog. Their existence here could only be assumed because of their presence in other bogs.

It was at the edge of the third stage that we turned back, for lack of footing. Probably this stage had got its start long ago when, somewhere along the margin of the water, some chance surface—a floating lily rhizome, a log, a thin mat of sedges, a bit of debris perhaps—offered an adequate though shallow seed bed for pioneer

SECOND STAGE
floating-leaved plants
along margin

plants. This group of floating pioneers soon offered a seedbed for others. Each time some root or rhizome or runner or arching branch, rooting at the tip, added a slight bit of substance to this thin mat, there was more support for more roots and rhizomes and arching branches. The mat was thickening. Bulrushes rode its wobbly surface, and cattails, and sphagnum moss, and swamp-loosestrife (*Decodon*), with its habit of arching and rooting from the nodes of the stem, and reed (*Phragmites*), and water speedwell (*Veronica anagallis-aquatica*), and water purslane (*Ludwigia palustris*), and forget-me-not (*Myosotis*). We, however, could not ride that fragile surface.

Even if we had been light-footed enough to advance farther, we should not have arrived at open water. That had long been arched over by the bulrush-decodon mat.

As soon as we had turned our backs on this insecurity, our oozing, muck-heavy footgear began to find a firmer foothold, but we felt as if we were treading a soggy spring mattress.

We had entered the fourth stage, often called the sedge, or the fen, stage. No longer were we surrounded entirely by sun-tolerant plants that can grow with their roots ever in water. On this thicker

THIRD STAGE
thin floating mat
composed of plants
that tolerate having their
roots always in water

mat there was opportunity for sun-tolerant plants that do not grow with their roots always in water. We lifted our ponderous feet past a variety of plants, including such well-known water-edgers as chairmaker's rush (*Scirpus americana*), as well as such inhabitants of dry places as aster and goldenrod. In this varied group appeared

FOURTH STAGE
thickening mat
plants that do not tolerate
having their roots always in water

grass of Parnassus (*Parnassia caroliniana*), white fringed orchid (*Habenaria leucophaea*), grass pink (*Calopogon pulchellus*), blazing star (*Liatris spicata*), Joe-Pye weed (*Eupatorium purpureum*), narrow-leaved loosestrife (*Steironema latifolium*), marsh redtop (*Calamagrostis canadensis*), and water-hemlock (*Cicuta maculata*). The fern of this fen stage was marsh shield fern (*Dryopteris thelypteris*).

In the fifth stage, where we had our fun jumping up and down to watch nearby shrubbery bobbing in unison, the bog began to develop a distinctive personality.

At that point we noticed that four major changes had appeared on the mat:

1. The plant society changed from an assemblage of familiar plants of a wide and general distribution, to an assemblage of plants of a limited distribution, some of them found only in bogs: pitcher plant, poison sumac, sphagnum moss.

2. Shrubs became a part of the mat. Some of them were outstanding examples of a limited distribution: cranberry, dwarf birch, poison sumac.

3. Something definite seemed to be happening to leaf form and texture. Many low shrubs showed small, thick, leathery, hoary leaves: cranberry, leatherleaf, bog rosemary.

4. Carnivorous plants had arrived, a strange pair of them: pitcher plant (*Sarracenia purpurea*), and sundew (*Drosera rotundifolia*).

Each of these four changes bespoke a changing condition in the bog:

The presence of plants of limited distribution spoke of conditions not generally a part of a plant's living conditions.

The coming in of shrubs spoke of a thickening mat.

The presence of small, thick, leathery, hoary leaves would ordinarily suggest a lack of water, but here they were growing on an oozing mat resting on water. In this instance they indicated that the water, though present, was not readily available, that this situation, while *physically wet* was *physiologically dry*.

The carnivorous plants were long an enigma. It has taken the work of a succession of famous botanists to arrive at our present understanding of the ways of these plants, and of their presence in a bog. If we were to look at the pitcher plant and sundew, as early botanists looked at them, through a gradually clearing fog of mystery, to witness the unfolding of what Emily Dickinson called "truth's superb surprise," we would see a succession of observations and experiments, as follows:

The story started long ago, before 1600, when someone made a drawing of the unique pitcher plant. That unexplained drawing traveled to Lisbon and Spain, before 1600, and then to Paris. There the botanist Carolus Clusius published a woodcut of it, in 1601, in his "Rariorum Plantarum Historia." In 1631 this woodcut was copied in Gerard's Herbal in England. Then, in 1640, an actual specimen of the pitcher plant arrived in England, brought home by the botanist, John Tradescant, from America. In 1699 Morison wrote about this enigmatic plant, but he apparently did not inspect it carefully, for he wrote that the lid of the leaf was hinged and movable. At about the same time Doctor M. S. Sarrazin sent a pressed specimen on a long trip by sailing vessel, from Quebec, to the French botanist, Tournefort. In 1700 Tournefort gave the plant a scientific name. He called it *Sarracenia*, after Doctor Sarrazin. By 1737 the system of Linnaeus was just beginning to gain acceptance. Linnaeus kept the name of *Sarracenia* for this plant, and added the species name of *purpurea*, for the purple coloring. The plant finally had its present scientific name *Sarracenia purpurea*.

But finding a name was easy compared with finding the function of the adaptation of this plant with leaves shaped like pitchers, with red-veined lips and watery contents where dead insects often floated.

In 1743, Mark Catesby, in the Carolinas, had a try at an explanation. He wrote that the pitcher-shaped leaves made a refuge for insects, so that the frogs could not eat them.

In 1791, two good Quaker botanists, William Bartram and Peter Collinson, objected to this interpretation. The insects seemed to be captured by the leaves, they argued, rather than protected. Those two were catching a gleam of light, but the fog of mystery was still thick, evidently, since Bartram added that the water in the leaves was "for the refreshment of the plant."

Presently two physicians, working independently more than fifty years apart, looked hard and long into those baffling pitchers. Doctor James MacBride noticed hairs, on the lip, pointing downward into the tube formed by the leaf; and also a viscid, fly-attracting substance at the mouth of the leaf. This was in 1817(18). The other physician,

J. H. Mellichamp, tried an experiment. He cut some bits of venison, placing part in one of the pitcher-like leaves, and part in a container of distilled water. He observed that the venison broke down faster in the pitcher-plant fluid, and decided that bacteria must be at work in the fluid. He noticed too, that flies did not seem able to escape from the pitcher-plant fluid so easily as from water. He concluded that the fluid had an "anaesthetic action." He noticed one other feature of the leaf, a sort of luring pathway of nectar leading up the outside of the pitcher. The work of Mellichamp blew away considerable fog in 1875(19).

Working at the same time as Mellichamp, Sir Joseph Hooker studied and made a summary of the findings of previous botanists (20). (Hooker's summary is the basis for the preceding accounts of studies of the pitcher plant.) Then he proceeded to inspect the leaf more minutely than anyone else had done. He saw that there were four distinct zones on the leaf, inside the pitcher.

> The first zone wore a red color, that same beefy red that seems to mark many flowers that attract flies. Hooker called this the "attractive zone."
> Just beneath this zone he saw another one with a surface broken by ridges directing insects downward, with only a little red coloring, and with many glands. This part Hooker called the "conducting zone."
> Beneath it was a glassy smooth stretch, with many glands. Hooker called it the "glandular zone."
> Beneath the glandular zone, lay zone four, with many long, glassy-smooth hairs, that gave no foothold to an insect. Hooker called this the "detentive zone."

Were this a witches' cauldron tale, instead of the story of an unpremeditating plant, how differently those four zones might be called:

> Zone 1 Come into my pretty parlor, my dear.
> Zone 2 Right this way, keep moving now, you!
> Zone 3 Ha, my proud beauty, in you go!
> Zone 4 Bubble, bubble, toil and trouble.

After Hooker, others, notably Francis Lloyd(21), have helped to brush away the remaining patches of fog.

71

Lloyd tells that zones one and two are not only attractive, but offer a treacherous foothold, which, together with the glassy surface of zone three, makes the *facilis descensus Averno*. He tells of experiments that showed zone four absorbing materials that zone three completely resisted. He calls zone four the "absorptive zone."

Lloyd recounts his experiment with a blue-bottle fly, and a pitcher plant leaf in a vial of water under a bell jar. The fly followed the nectar path on the outside of the leaf to the rim. Then he began to sip nectar, gradually reaching further and further down, but always hanging on to the lid or the rim with at least one hind foot. But that treacherous surface betrayed him, every time. The

PITCHER
PLANT
Sarracenia
purpurea

reason this fly was privileged to make the trip more than once was that Lloyd had cut a door for his escape, just above the surface of the water. Twelve times that same fly made that same trip.

Other experimenters, Hepburn, Jones, and St. Johns(22), flushed out the pitchers, emptied them, and then added fresh water. They let this stand in the pitchers for several days. Then they poured the liquid out and put fibrin into it. They found that the fluid could certainly digest the fibrin. Then they examined the pitchers for bacteria in their fluid. In open pitchers they found bacteria always present, but working so slowly as to be of little importance in digestion as compared with the fluid itself. These experimenters then added substances that would help them trace the absorption of the digested material. They found that the nitrogenous substances in the fluid were absorbed more rapidly than the water.

72

While these and many other plant scientists were examining the leaves of the pitcher plant, others were experimenting with the glistening gluey leaves of its small companion, the sundew.

In 1779, Doctor Roth, in Bremen, took an ant in a pair of tweezers, and placed it carefully in the middle of a sundew leaf.

The ant seemed unable to pull away from the gleaming globules at the tips of the hairs. His feet pulled the sticky substance like taffy as he struggled. Then the hairs began to bend inward, folding themselves over the ant. He died in fifteen minutes.

SUNDEW
Drosera
rotundifolia

In 1852, Milde timed the whole carnivorous operation. He placed small flies on the leaves, and found that the tentacles started bending in five minutes. By the next day the entire leaf was bent around the insect. In five days the leaf was open again.

Later Darwin and others demonstrated that dead bodies do not provoke so much response as living ones, and inorganic bodies, such as particles of sand, do not stimulate the flow of mucilage, or cause the hairs to move in any way.

Francis Darwin continued his father's investigations, growing sundew plants in two lots, one fed with insects, the other unfed. The fed plants were more vigorous, had more and stronger flowers, and more and much heavier seeds.

The work with carnivorous plants described here, and much additional experimentation, is recounted in greater detail by Lloyd in a book devoted to carnivorous plants(21). He concludes his study of the sundew by saying, "There can, therefore, be no sort of doubt that the ability to absorb substances (mineral salts as well as nitrogen) is of significance to the plant."

Are there any other plants that have had as long a line of distinguished plant scientists concerned in building up an explanation of their mechanism? With these investigators revealing that the plants do trap insects, do digest them, do absorb nitrogen and other nutrients from their bodies, and do profit by that absorption, the operation of carnivorous plants is no longer an enigma.

Understanding *how* they work makes it not too difficult to find a probable reason *why* they work in a bog—a place where there exists a deficiency in the nutrients that they obtain from insects.

FIFTH STAGE
poor aeration
shrubs
carnivorous plants

That deficiency is caused by lack of drainage. The lack of drainage causes poor aeration, resulting in a deficient growth of bacteria, and the consequent accumulation of plant debris, and the gradual development of an acid condition. As the bacteria population is reduced, the nitrogen becomes less available; and, as acidity increases, the ability of the plant to absorb through its root hairs, by osmosis, is decreased.

Existing under these conditions there could only be a limited assemblage, plants that cannot compete with others in more favored situations, but can have a place here if they can tolerate it. Each plant must have some special adaptation to be a part of this group; the carnivorous plants just happen to have the most dramatic adaptation.

In that tough community we lingered awhile, realizing that we should not be meeting these specialized individuals for a long time, probably. We fed mosquitoes to the pitcher plants, and irritated the tentacles of the sundew. Then we dug up a plant of each to see if their roots were as insignificant as might be expected of plants that had established a new intake. They were, and the plants were easy to set back into their small soggy places.

As we continued on our way, we found ourselves not so much walking as jumping, from root hummock to root hummock. These were the roots of trees, the first tree to come in on the bog mat, the tamarack or American larch.

Each island of tamarack roots gave us a foothold that was less soggy than the area we had left behind. We were in the sixth stage of the bog. A new element was shade. On the hummocks shade-

SIXTH STAGE
shade
tamarack trees
root hummocks

tolerant plants such as jewelweed (*Impatiens biflora*) appeared. Among the mosses, sphagnum was replaced by the moss, *Mnium*. Among the ferns, marsh shield fern was replaced by royal fern (*Osmunda regalis*).

We could see that these hummocks were formed by a surprisingly shallow root system, because the wind had recently toppled two trees over, tipping on edge a flat platter of roots, the shape of the brown pool they had uncorked in the mat.

In the low places between the root-islands, a few poison sumacs still persisted, as did several other plants of earlier stages.

We were soon through with hummock-hopping, and moving on to earth that felt firm beneath our feet. This was the seventh stage of the bog. The mat had thickened considerably, and supported a rich forest, with abundant yellow birch, white pine, red maple, and arborvitae. Shade was more dense, and shade-tolerant plants abundant: serviceberry (*Amelanchier canadensis*), white violet (*Viola blanda*), showy lady's slipper (*Cypripedium reginae*), stemless lady's slipper (*Cypripedium acaule*), wild sarsaparilla (*Aralia nudicaulis*), cinnamon fern (*Osmunda cinnamomea*) most conspicuous of all, spinulose wood fern (*Aspidium spinulosum*) and an assemblage of typical northerners. That assemblage included partridgeberry (*Mitchella repens*), starflower (*Trientalis americana*), Indian cucumber-root (*Medeola virginiana*), bunchberry (*Cornus canadensis*).

SEVENTH STAGE
more dense shade
thick mat
rich forest

sugar maple
tamarack
poison sumac
sedge
bulrush

From among the ferns and northerners we climbed up on to the road, and then to the welcome dryness of the dune. We sat among black oaks, blueberries, and sassafras, removing black muck from our footgear, and looking back down at the bog.

What was that assemblage of northerners doing, across the road from black oaks and sassafras?

To find a similar assemblage we might have traveled either to another bog of our area, or to the north woods.

These bog spots of northern vegetation are considered glacial relics left behind in the midst of conditions that the natural vegetation of the area cannot tolerate, but that the vegetation of the north is able to tolerate. Evidently plants that are able to survive when soil water is locked up by freezing, can survive just as well when it is locked up by acidity.

Not all bogs lie, like the one described here, in deep depressions. In southern Michigan are several bogs that lie in shallow depressions, demonstrating that it is lack of drainage rather than depth of depression that is the essential feature for bog formation. Because those sand-locked depressions are so shallow, they do not show the successive stages of a bog in a deep depression, but have one and the same stage overall. Near Stevensville, Michigan, one may visit a bog that is in the waterlily (second) stage; another that is in the sedge (fourth) stage; another that is in the leatherleaf-cranberry (fifth) stage; and another that is already completely covered with tamarack, representing the sixth stage.

In northern Wisconsin, as a part of summer field work, we once spent an amazing day on a great bog that showed another variation. We set out in the morning on the open water, in rowboats, each boat containing three botany students.

Ahead of us were islands, an imposing flotilla of them.

An island came bobbing alongside our rowboat. It consisted of a floating log, with a minute tamarack seedling riding it, in a crack beside a knob of moss.

Then we passed another island and hauled it close for inspection. Two logs, some branches, and some brown matted vegetation were entangled to make the base for this island. Riding it was a good stand of bulrush, a handful of sphagnum moss, a small plant of leatherleaf, and two minute rosettes of sundew.

Ahead floated islands with trees—tamaracks. Each boatload chose an island for its own special study. Then someone landed to test the island to see whether it would support three people without bobbing too precariously. If it would, then the other two disembarked, and the identification and listing of every bit of vegetation were begun.

When we had completed the listing on our island, we could not resist a gleeful ten minutes of jumping up and down on opposite sides to make a sort of see-saw. Then we left, and joined the other islanders to compare lists.

FLOATING
ISLAND
C

They were almost identical, and almost the same as our lists from the Mineral Springs bog. The bog conditions were the same, but the mat of the Wisconsin lake was being formed in patches, as well as by extension from the edges.

That was in 1914.

We took great pleasure in reading the story written in bogs where we found them. We did not realize that we were reading only a small part of the available record. We did not know that our book was upside down and we were reading only the events recorded on the last few pages.

Today, when you talk about a bog to a botanist, he is very likely to ask, "Has it been bored?"

No one asked us that in 1914, because no one was conscious of the fact that we were walking over layer upon layer of ancient pollen, scattered through peat formed of plant remains—pollen waiting to reveal its record.

But over in Sweden, G. Lagerheim had already suspected the existence of this record, and had written about it, in Swedish, in 1909.

By 1916, another Swede, von Post, was working out the methods for boring bogs and deciphering their story.(2)

During this phase, Auer bored a Canadian bog.(1) And then started a line of bog investigations, with Fuller(7), Sears(6), Potzger, (8, 10), Hansen and Cain, leading in this country. This has been a rich field for Master's Degree papers, and for Doctor's degrees. In 1927, according to Cain(11), there were about 150 publications on this subject and in 1944 about 2500.

The procedure in a bog investigation is, in general, like this:

A plant scientist goes out on a bog, carrying a peat borer, some bottles for samples, and provision for washing the borer. He has previously spent some time ascertaining the deepest part of the bog.

He starts boring at that spot. The borer is a hollow cylinder surrounded by a movable sleeve. This sleeve has a cutting edge at the opening in the side of the cylinder. He bores the cylinder down to just one foot below the surface, and reverses the handle. That closes the opening. He brings the borer out.

He takes a sample from the core, being careful to take it from the center to avoid any danger of its being contaminated.

He puts the sample into a bottle, and labels it with the name of the bog, and the depth. Then he washes the borer carefully, and takes a second boring, two feet down, treating it in the same way.

Again and again he takes his sample, one foot deeper each time. Finally he runs into gritty sand or mud. There he stops boring. He has reached the original bottom of the depression.

Now he takes his borings into the laboratory. He examines the last one first—the one taken perhaps twenty, thirty, fifty, or one hundred feet down.

He prepares the peat sample by placing it in a solution of 95% alcohol, or 12% potassium hydroxide. Then he inspects it under a high-powered microscope. There may be as many as 50,000 to 1,000,000 pollen grains in one gram of the peat. But he does not consider all of them. He counts out 200 of them. (Some investigators count only 100 for each foot level.)

The plant scientist now is ready to identify the kinds of plants (usually trees) that these 200 pollen grains came from. He probably has slides of labeled pollen grains at hand for comparison.

After he has counted out and identified 200 grains from each specimen of peat, that is, one from each foot level, he is ready to read the story of the bog, or rather, he is ready to read the story *in* the bog. For this is the record that the bog has kept of the vegetation that has marched past on the surrounding hills.

In his first specimen the pollen grains are chiefly of one kind, balsam fir (*Abies balsamea*). If he is working on an Illinois bog, he realizes that conditions must have been very different when that pollen sifted down into the water. Not only does balsam fir fail to grow naturally in Illinois, but it also refuses to thrive for all the vacationers who bring home vigorous young trees from northern Wisconsin, shriveling instead, before the prairie winds.

There is probably some spruce pollen together with the fir pollen, and perhaps a small quantity of pine, and hemlock.

Those pollen grains fell like rain onto the open water of this lake soon after the glacier receded. They were probably laid down about 10,000 years ago. The forest that had been driven south by the glacier was moving north on its very heels. Around the lake the hills were covered with the narrow spires of the balsam fir. Probably little life had begun in the cold waters of the lake.

As the investigator reads the record in his pollen grains, he finds that the fir pollen soon begins to decrease, and the spruce to increase. There is not much pine. Remembering that it is much easier to grow a healthy white spruce tree in northern Illinois or

I After the glacier retreated, balsam fir came in

pollen rain

balsam fir   🌲
balsam fir pollen 🟤

pollen deposit

II Fir moved north, spruce came in

pollen rain

white spruce   🌲
white spruce pollen ᘔᘔᘔ

pollen deposit

III Spruce moved north, pine came in

pollen rain

pine 🌲
pine pollen ••••

pollen deposit

IV Pine moved north, oak came in

pollen rain

oak 🌳
oak pollen ++++

pollen deposit

V Oak stayed

pollen rain

some pine left ↗
behind on bog mat

pollen deposit

Indiana today, than to grow a healthy fir, he visualizes the conditions then as being still cold, but a little less moist.

As he continues to read upward through the pollen record, he finds fir dropping off in importance from foot level to foot level, with spruce decreasing, too, and pine increasing, and oak beginning to be a part of the count. Probably, he concludes, the climate is growing warmer and drier.

By the time he has examined the record in one fourth of the bottles, he finds that fir and spruce pollen are no longer present. Pine has increased greatly, and there is more oak pollen than any other kind. It is growing still warmer and drier.

Then oak pollen increases in importance and pine decreases. As the pine forest moves north, leaving the hills to an oak forest, and hickory, a few pines are left, together with other relicts, on the bog mat.

The forest stays just about the same up to the present time, with a slight tendency toward an increase of pine pollen, indicating that there is a slight change in the climate toward a cooler, moister period.

Peat bog records agree in their story of the past. Whether they are in North America or in Europe, their story is essentially the same, and includes the following major events:

1. When the glacier receded there followed a *cool, moist period*, indicated by *fir* pollen.

2. Then came a period of *increasing warmth* indicated by increase of *pine pollen*.

3. Then came a warm, dry period (often called the xerothermic period) indicated by an abundance of pine pollen in one bog; oak pollen in another; and pollen of dry-land herbs in another, depending on the location of the bog.

4. Then came a long period of stability, comprising about three fourths of the total record—a period of warmth, but not so dry as the preceding period, indicated by pollens of the same kind as the present forest of the area.

5. And recently there has been a hint of decreasing warmth,

indicated by a slight increase in pollens representing a more northern vegetation.

In all bogs there is some unidentified pollen, and some pollen in too small quantity to be of any importance. Some allowance must be made for pollen that blows in from a distance; and for the fact that some pollen is more perishable than others; and for the fact that some trees produce pollen in greater quantities than others; and for pollens that are insect-borne rather than wind-borne.

Some bogs have shown a thin black page in their records, a "black bookmark," one of the outstanding bog authorities calls it (10). This is interpreted as being the record of fire.

As we read the pollen record of bog after bog, we naturally begin to wonder, "How long did it take for all these layers to accumulate?"

Since pollen records have indicated that the forests may have come in within 50 miles of the edge of the retreating ice sheet,(7) we could be justified in figuring the age of bog pollen from the time of the retreat of the ice sheet.

But, our dating of the ice sheet has recently been revolutionized. Trees, buried by the glacier in southern Wisconsin, were examined in order to learn how much radio-activity had been lost from their radio-active carbon. The results indicated that the glacier that killed them came, not 25,000 years ago, but only 11,000 years ago.

Why not let this tell-tale "Carbon 14" date some of the pollen from a bog?

That is exactly what is being done. Samples of peat from eight feet down in the Quetico-Superior region were sent to Dr. W. F. Libby and Dr. J. R. Arnold of the University of Chicago. The answer came back. The pollen in that eight-foot layer drifted down from the trees 7128 years ago, possibly 300 years earlier, possibly 300 years later. From that figure Potzger estimated(10) that it took 500 years (on an average) to lay down one foot of pollen in the Lake Superior region. This, he points out, shows us "that several generations of forests developed and died while one foot of peat was laid down."

And now that scientists have gradually deciphered these bog records: the plant succession on a floating mat; the meaning of carnivorous plants; the northward march of forests; the changing climate; the time-clock; and archeologists have made use of pollen analysis for dating such relics of the past as a ruin in Mexico(17), and a human sacrifice of 2000 years ago in a Danish bog(16)—now one is inclined to wonder if that is all, or if there is still ore to be learned from this "history book with the flexible cover.

REFERENCES

1. "Peat Bogs in Southeastern Canada" by V. Auer. *Department of Mines, Geological Survey* 162 (1930), 1-32.
2. "Problems and Working Lines in the Post-Arctic Forest History of Northern Europe" by L. von Post. In *Report of Proceedings of the Fifth International Botanical Congress* (48-54), University Press, Cambridge, 1930.
3 "Pollen Statistics" by G. Erdtmann. *Science* 73, (1931), 399-401.
4. "Pleistocene Forests of Illinois" by John Voss. *Botanical Gazette* 94 (1933), 808-814.
5. "Postglacial Migration of Forests in Illinois, Wisconsin, and Minnesota," by John Voss. *Botanical Gazette* 95 (1934), 33-43.
6. "Types of North American Pollen Profiles" by Paul B. Sears. *Ecology* 16 (1935), 488-499.
7. "Postglacial Vegetation of the Lake Michigan Region" by George D. Fuller. *Ecology* 16 (July, 1935), 473-487.
8. "Pollen Study of Five Bogs in Price and Sawyer Counties, Wisconsin," by J. E. Potzger. *Butler University Botanical Studies* 6 (May, 1943), 54-64.
9. "A Comparative Study of Three Indiana Bogs" by Carl O. Keller. *Butler University Botanical Studies* 6 (May, 1943), 65-80.
10. *Bogs of the Quetico-Superior Country Tell Its Forest History* by J. E. Potzger. The President's Quetico-Superior Committee, (919 N. Michigan Avenue) Chicago, 1950.
11. "Pollen Analysis as a Paleoecological Research Method" by Stanley Cain. In his book *Foundations of Plant Geography*, Harper, New York, 1944.
12. "Pollen Succession in the Sediments of Singletary Lake, North Carolina," by David G. Frey. *Ecology* 32 (1951), 518-533.
13. "Pollen Profiles from Southeastern Alaska" by Calvin J. Heusser. *Ecological Monographs* 22 (1952), 33-352.

14. "Regional Aspects of the Late-Glacial and Post-Glacial Pollen Succession of Southeastern North Carolina" by David G. Frey. *Ecological Monographs* **23** (1953), 289-314.
15. "Radiocarbon Dating of Late Pleistocene Events" by Richard Foster Flint and Edward S. Deevey, Jr. *American Journal of Science* **249** (1951), 257-300.
16. "Lifelike Man Preserved 2000 Years in Peat, A Danish Bog Yields Remains of a Human Sacrifice That Helps Reconstruct the Life Of Europe's Ancient Tribes," by Peter Vilhelm Glob. *The National Geographic Magazine* **105** (March, 1954), 419-430.
17. "Pollen Analysis and Mexican Archeology" by Edward S. Deevey. *American Antiquity* **15**, 135-149.
18. "On the Power of *Sarracenia* to Entrap Insects" a letter by James MacBride, (read before Linnean Society on December 19, 1815). *Transactions of The Linnean Society of London* **12** (1818), 48-52.
19. "Notes on *Sarracenia variolaris*" by J. H. Millechamp. *Proceedings of the American Association for the Advancement of Science* (1875), 113-133.
20. "Address" by John Dalton Hooker to British Association for the Advancement of Science, in Belfast, 1874. *Report of the Meetings of the British Association for the Advancement of Science* (1875), 102-116.
21. *The Carnivorous Plants* by Francis Ernest Lloyd. The Chronica Botanica Company, Waltham, Mass., 1942.
22. "The Biochemistry of the American Pitcher Plants" by J. S. Hepburn, F. M. Jones, and Elizabeth Q. St. John. *Transactions of the Wagner Free Institute of Science* **11** (1927), 1-95.

5.

CANYON STORY
or
Following a Stream in Southern Indiana

THE upland forest where we walked gave no hint of a canyon in its future.

"This is undissected topography," said our geologist.

We were looking for the birthplace of a stream. We had learned that the streams there at Turkey Run, Indiana, have it in their destiny to shape a ravine in their mud-pie childhood, and then knife out a canyon in their whittling youth, before their waters find middle-age spread in Sugar Creek, and old-age resignation in the Wabash.

We wanted to see the whole story—indeed we hoped to find the upland forest pregnant with a canyon not yet born.

But we dallied there, basking in the sunset of summer that emanated from that forest in four bands of brilliance. Highest was the layered canopy of beeches and sugar maples. Beneath them were spread the red-fruited shelves of flowering dogwood. Farther down came the wine color of maple-leaved viburnum. And then there was the forest floor with its herbs and ferns among the fallen leaves.

We walked for a long time in that rich beech-maple forest. Then, abruptly, we found that we were under white oaks. There was only a narrow belt dominated by them, but the trees were of imposing age and size.

No sooner had we commented on this change in the aspect of the canopy than we found ourselves in a belt of still more marked change. Our footsteps made a drier sound. The four-layered aspect was gone. There was only one layer, the canopy of hemlock branches.

A four-layered forest

sugar maple

beech

flowering dogwood

maple-leaved viburnum

maidenhair fern

A beech and maple forest, then a white oak forest, and then a hemlock forest. It was as if, with a few mighty strides, we had stepped home to the woods of northern Illinois; and then had stepped further north, into a summer camp site in northern Wisconsin.

We continued no further in that direction because, beyond the narrow band of hemlocks, the canyon gaped. Most of the hemlocks were astride its very rim.

We walked among the clutching hemlocks, and suddenly, where there was a break in their dark canopy, we noticed that our feet were treading the green tooled-leather forest floor of northern Wisconsin, or northern Michigan, or Maine.

Crimson partridgeberries shone among those polished leaves, and

87

wintergreen berries, and even the coral-red translucent fruits of yew. We had not needed to travel north to find these plants, because the cold north had delivered them down here long, long ago, driving them south before the icy cold threat of the advancing glacier.

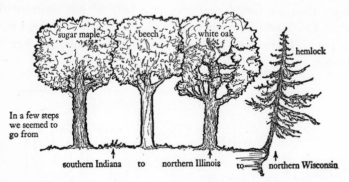

In a few steps
we seemed to
go from

southern Indiana   to   northern Illinois   to   northern Wisconsin

But the retreat of the glacier had everywhere allowed plants to creep slowly back to their old homes.

How, then, did it happen that this little band of northerners, acquainted with the song of the hermit thrush, the drum of the

A little band
of northerners

wintergreen

partridgeberry

yew   hemlock

mighty pileated woodpecker, and the big feet of the snowshoe rabbit, should be isolated here, left behind to hobnob with wood thrushes, and red-bellied woodpeckers, and cottontail rabbits? And why must the northerners cling to the cliff's edge, as though the white oaks were pushing from behind, while the beeches and maples in turn pushed the white oaks?

The time was when they did not need to cling to the cliff's edge. That was when the glacier retreated. During this period probably the upland was dominated by a forest of hemlock and other conifers, with a forest floor covered with trailing arbutus, wintergreen, partridgeberry, and yew. As it grew warmer, the oaks and hickories began to come in, wherever a squirrel had buried a nut and had forgotten where he put it. Some hemlocks survived this invasion—those that happened to grow near the canyon's edge. It is drier there because some ground water escapes through the canyon wall.

The forest of oak and hickory covered the upland, but did not invade the dry edge of the canyon. But presently the oak-hickory forest, in turn, found itself nursing upstarts, changelings, that were not its own offspring. The wind had brought seeds of sugar maples, and squirrels had brought beech nuts. The maple and beech seedlings throve in the accumulated leaf mold, and tolerated the heavy shade.

Then the beeches and maples began to weave a denser shade, denser than white oak seedlings can tolerate. In time the forest of beech and maple took over all of the upland except the drier belt just behind the hemlock edge.

The white oaks cannot move back in among the beeches and maples, no matter if squirrels do carry their acorns back and bury them and forget them. The shade is too dense for their survival. Nor can the hemlocks reinvade that upland territory, no matter if the wind does carry thousands of their seeds back there. It has been found that hemlock seeds do not succeed in rooting in the thick ground cover of rotting leaves(2).

We turned back toward the beech-maple forest. We had not intended to see the canyon full grown before seeing its birth and its youth. As we walked away from the canyon's brink, we passed, in addition to the change in tree dominants, five other changes.

The soil water in the deeper layers increased markedly.

The tree roots changed from shallow to deep.

The soil acidity decreased(4).

The herbs of the forest floor changed from those that are typically acid-tolerant (cushion moss, reindeer lichen, pine-tree moss, partridgeberry) to those that are not typically acid-tolerant (downy yellow violet, ginseng, jewelweed, wild phlox).

The number of species on the forest floor changed from few to many.

The last two of these five changes, we could easily observe for ourselves. The first three we had read about, in the careful reports of research students from Butler University (1, 2, 3, 4).

We walked for a long time, deep into the beech-maple forest.

The canyon was born among maiden-hair ferns

"Here is a boulder," said the geologist. "Granite. Brought down from Canada probably, by the glacier. We are on glacial till, here."

Beside the boulder grew two plants especially characteristic of the beech-maple forest. One was the northern beech fern; the other was the strange pinkish-tan growth of beechdrops, the saprophyte that has earned its name from its habit of growing on the roots of beech trees.

We found ourselves treading carefully among ferns—silvery spleenwort, rattlesnake fern, fragile fern, narrow-leaved spleenwort, and Christmas fern. Aristocrat among them was the maidenhair, with its mahogany stem upholding a horizontal green swirl.

"Here, I believe, is the place we have been looking for," said the geologist, pointing to a shallow, temporary sort of pool that held last night's rain.

"Want to see the small beginning of what may some day become

90

a canyon?" The geologist walked around to the soggy side of the dish, to the debris that held the rain back, and kicked it out.

The barrier, without our help, would have broken soon. We merely speeded events up by a week, or a month or so, depending on the force of the rains.

"If we could wait here long enough," said the geologist, "we might see that scratch in the upland deepen and extend, until these woods became dissected, first by a ravine, cutting down through the glacial drift, and then by a canyon cutting down through the bed-rock beneath. Since we haven't time to wait for the canyon, or even for the ravine, we will follow this water and see the succession of events."

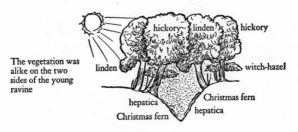

The vegetation was alike on the two sides of the young ravine

hickory   linden   hickory
linden   witch-hazel
hepatica   Christmas fern
Christmas fern   hepatica

The released water had disappeared at once, down an obscure little draw. We followed. There was only a formless, indefinite depression among the thin-leaved spleenworts and the jewelweed; slight at first, but deepening quickly to a furrow, cutting down into the glacial clay.

"The V-shaped stage of a youthful stream," said the geologist.

Both sides of the young ravine were rich in growth, with shagbark hickory, linden, witch-hazel, bedstraw, and abundant Christmas fern. There seemed to be no difference between the vegetation of the two sides, not even where one of them had a direct south exposure.

The ravine broadened gradually, and deepened, too. It was cutting down through the soft layers of shale that underlay the glacial till.

"Pennsylvanian coal measures," labeled the geologist, crumbling a bit of the shale in her hands.

For a while the ravine ran directly east and west. We could now see distinct differences between the north-facing and the south-facing slopes. On the north-facing slope were wild ginger, maidenhair ferns, thin-leaved spleenwort, hepaticas, blue beech. On the south-facing slope were sassafras, agrimony, catbrier, wild aster, wild currant, goldenrod.

The ravine deepened and widened still more.

"The U-shaped stage," said the geologist.

Differences between the north- and the south-facing sides became still more pronounced. There were more oaks on the south-facing, and more sugar maples on the north-facing side.

The north-facing and south-facing sides were different

blue beech
hepatica
wild ginger

sassafras
catbrier
agrimony
wild currant

Presently the stream began to wander on the floor of its ravine, depositing a small flood plain on the slow inner side of each curve, and cutting into a shaly bluff on the outer side.

"The meandering stream stage," said the geologist. "The speed of the stream and its downcutting power have slowed considerably."

At this point there were three different types of vegetation: the north-facing slopes were clothed in beech, and an abundance of Christmas fern; the south-facing slope wore white oak, and considerable hepatica; and on the bottom were nettle (*Laportea*), moonseed (*Menispermum*), and hog-peanut (*Amphicarpa*).

The stream had reached a sort of middle age. Its waters were held in a quiet pool. Had this stream continued to cut down through soft materials, its next stage would have been placid old age.

But that was not to happen in this case, we found, when we looked over the barrier that held back the pool.

Suddenly, delightfully, the stream, plunging over the barrier, renewed its youth. The waters that had been so sluggish, now took to whittling again. The stream had cut down through the soft shale, and reached the underlying sandstone.

"Mansfield sandstone," remarked the geologist, "a durable building stone."

As the stream plunged over the hard ledge of sandstone into the bowl that it had gouged for itself below, leaving the middle-aged ravine behind, and beginning life anew in a very young canyon, we too went over the ledge, but more slowly, taking our middle age along with us.

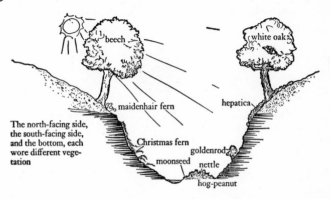

beech
white oak
maidenhair fern
hepatica
The north-facing side, the south-facing side, and the bottom, each wore different vegetation
Christmas fern
goldenrod
moonseed
nettle
hog-peanut

"The V-shaped stage of a young stream again," said the geologist, "but now it is cutting through rock instead of glacial till."

It was cool and shady and windless down there. The term "vapor pocket" was easy to understand, as we stood moistly astride the narrow, swift stream, with our hands braced on each side against dripping mosses, and looked up through a canopy of hemlock boughs.

We were in the domain of the rock-carpeting plants, called "belly-floppers" by one young observer. These are the plants that plaster themselves prone against the moist rock.

Dominant among them were the liverworts. There was an unusual representation of their kind on the moist vertical walls;

Marchantia, Conocephalum, Reboulia, Anthoceros, Porella. (The smaller a plant is, the longer its name seems to be. Aren't plants that get short names mostly those that are eaten, or taken for ailments, or grown in cottage gardens?)

The fern-leaved moss, *Thuidium delicatulum,* held close to the rock wall, and so did *Mnium cuspidatum,* and *Umbilicaria,* or rock tripe, which incidentally can be eaten. From every ledge the bulblet bladder fern dripped down.

It was moist and new and young there in the steep-sided narrow canyon. Moist and new, like the conditions on the young earth when the first primitive plants came ashore. And there beside us, right at eye level, were the plants that resemble, probably better than do any other living plants, those first land plants.

Both sides were the same again — bulblet bladder fern — liverworts — mosses

"Apparently the Christopher Columbus of the plant kingdom was a liverwort," says Coulter, in his "Story of the Plant Kingdom" (10).

And although the ages since that first successful landing have carried living green to the tops of the driest hills and to the tips of the highest trees, the liverwort form still persists, providing us with a picture of the probable architecture of the first plant that managed to survive on land. Perhaps it was stranded in a tidal basin; and perhaps many others, stranded at the same time, perished, while this one rugged individual somehow survived, desperately suckling the spray-drenched sand.

We lifted one of the liver-shaped ribbons from the moist rock surface to look at its underside, and saw the tentative prophecy

94

of roots scattered on the green skin. Not real roots, any more than the green ribbons were real leaves; but we felt that to hold a liverwort in our hands was to hold both a record of the past, because of its resemblance to the platelike alga that must have been its ancestor in the sea, and a promise of the future, because of this suggestion of roots, and the thin protective skin.

We looked for a long time, in spite of our soggy feet, at the assemblage of liverworts, as we reconstructed the coming of green to the barren, stony earth. We saw that where liverworts had prepared the way and made a foothold on the canyon wall, the

Liverworts prepare the way for mosses

Mosses prepare the way for ferns

mosses had come in. Some of the mosses were prone like the liverworts, but others held their bit of green free from contact with the rock. We were reading the second chapter in the invasion of the land.

It was not far that the mosses lifted themselves from the rock surface. It could not be far, because they had not yet acquired tubes for carrying water up through their structures; and because their sperms must still swim in order to fertilize the ovum, as the sperms swam in the liverworts before them, and in the algae before the liverworts.

As we inspected the canyon wall, we saw how often, where mosses had prepared the way by laying down their plush carpet, the ferns had come in. No need for these to be prostrate, no need for these to cling so close to the water supply, for the ferns have tubes, a vascular system, for carrying water.

We were reading the third chapter in the invasion of the land.

We looked at the delicate bulblet bladder fern, realizing that it was but a pygmy representative of that great widespread group of ferns and fern allies that helped lay down the coal measures.

It seemed to us as if we were looking at plants that had graduated from the rock-carpeting class, until we remembered that the first stage in the life history of a fern is a tiny heart-shaped prothallium, resembling a liverwort, plastered close against the moist rock, and having sperms that still must swim.

Up above our heads, the hemlock branches represented the fourth chapter in the invasion of the land, the naked-seed plants. Crowding the hemlocks from behind, we knew, were the white oaks, representing the fifth chapter in the invasion, the enclosed-seed plants.

"Not only," ventured the geologist, "do the plants in this narrow canyon take us through the pages of a botany textbook, but they take us through several geological periods as well.

"The first invasion of the land by plants probably took place in the Silurian period, about 400 million years ago. Turkey Run was under the Niagaran Sea then, and trilobites were shucking off their hard three-lobed skins around here, and cephalopods were waving their tentacles from the open ends of their ice-cream-cone-shaped shells.

"The first seed-bearing plants appeared in the Devonian period, but did not amount to much. Turkey Run had primitive fish swimming over it then.

"The fern ancestors dominated the land in the Carboniferous period, while this sandstone that forms our canyon wall was being laid down along the margin of a shallow sea.

"The conifers appeared in the Triassic period, about 200 million years ago. Turkey Run was land then. Probably there were dinosaurs lumbering around here.

"The enclosed-seed plants appeared in the Cretaceous period, about 120 million years ago. Turkey Run could have been making acquaintance of marsupials with their pouches full of offspring at that time."

A dark little newt slithered across the bed of liverwort and moss.

"How fitting," said the geologist, "a representative of the first

96

animal group to come ashore, scampering across the first land plants—amphibians both of them."

Our shoes were too wet, so we moved on down the canyon. Now the walls stood farther apart. The stream had slowed down.

"The U-shaped stage of the canyon," said the geologist.

No longer was the vegetation of north- and south-facing walls alike, now that they were too far apart to shelter each other from wind and sun. The north-facing wall was still dark green with liverworts, mosses, and bladder fern. But the south-facing wall wore a thin covering of gray-green. That covering was composed of lichens, the typical pioneers of dry rocks.

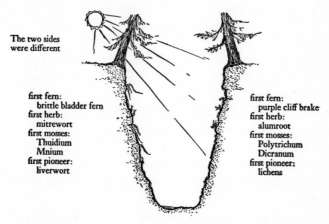

The two sides were different

first fern:
 brittle bladder fern
first herb:
 mitrewort
first mosses:
 Thuidium
 Mnium
first pioneer:
 liverwort

first fern:
 purple cliff brake
first herb:
 alumroot
first mosses:
 Polytrichum
 Dicranum
first pioneer:
 lichens

The mosses that were coming in where lichens had prepared the way were different from the mosses that came in where liverworts had preceded them; they were *Polytrichum piliferinum*, and *Dicranum scoparium*. The first fern was different too; it was purple cliff brake, leathery and tough.

The first abundant herb on the north-facing side was a mitrewort, *Mitella;* on the south-facing side it was alumroot, *Heuchera hispida*. The difference in the feel of these two plants, the one tender and silky, the other harsh and hispid, was the difference in feel between plants characteristic of moist shady places, and those of hot, dry areas.

97

The canyon continued to broaden.

In places where the edge of the cliff had given way and formed a talus slope, the north-facing talus slopes had young sugar maple clothing them, together with linden and ash, and an abundant growth of hepaticas, running euonymus, spikenard, and maidenhair and Christmas ferns. Incidentally, when that cliff edge had slid down, the last foothold of the hemlocks was gone.

Opposite this rich talus-slope community, a south-facing talus-slope was sparsely clothed in big-tooth aspen (*Populus grandidentata*).

The canyon had a bottom now, where asters and goldenrods were finding conditions much like those by the side of a road. As the bottom broadened, the stream ambled along, forming a flood plain, first on one side, then on the other, and then on both.

"The meandering stage again," the geologist reminded us.

Here grew plants that could utilize the summer for growing after the spring freshets subsided—nettle, smartweed, giant ragweed.

By the time the stream entered Sugar Creek, it was moving placidly and creating flood plains on both sides. Along these flood plains, smartweed and ragweed occupied the wettest parts, those most recently deposited along the river's edge. The areas that were a little older, a little drier, a little farther back from the stream bed, had as their first woody plant the sand-bar willow, which formed a shrubby thicket. Where the willows had prepared the way and the ground had better aeration, the sycamores came in; and after that, the cottonwoods and silver maples.

Black maple came next, together with a rich undergrowth, containing jewelweed and Jack-in-the-pulpit.

No longer was the vegetation abruptly divided into different types of communities by canyon walls. Instead, the tumbled slopes of material that had once been canyon walls graded imperceptibly into the margins of the flood-plain; while the upland forest spilled slowly down the slopes to grade into the flood-plain forest.

Following the black maple came walnuts, with spice-bush, grape fern, and some leatherwood.

CANYON DISSECTING A BEECH-MAPLE UPLAND FOREST COMMUNITY

A

Young V-Shaped Canyon

Same plants on both walls
liverworts
↓ mosses:—Thuidium, Mnium
↓ fern, bulblet bladder fern
↓ shrub, spikenard

North-Facing Wall

liverworts

mosses:
↓ Thuidium
↓ Mnium
↓ Catharinea

bulblet bladder fern
↓ mitrewort

spikenard
↓

red maple
↓

white ash
↓

American
elm
↓
sugar
maple
↓
beech

U-Shaped Stage

B

Meandering Stage

Flood-Plain Stage

X

**South-
Facing
Wall**

lichens

mosses:
↓ Polytrichum
↓ Dicranum

fern:
purple cliff
brake
↓

alumroot
↓

big-tooth aspen
↓

red mulberry
↓

white ash
↓

American elm
↓

sugar maple
↓

beech

Bottom

Succession starting at B
aster goldenrod
smartweed
sand-bar willow
sycamore
cottonwood and silver maple
black maple

Where shade was deepening we found a few young sugar maples; and, finally, a scattering of beech seedlings.

The circle was very nearly completed. We were almost back in a beech-maple forest. We had followed the stream from its small beginning under beeches, through its vigorous canyon-forming youth, to its slow-moving old age with the beech-maple forest trickling down around it. The childhood and old age of a stream, like the childhood and old age of a human being, seem to have much in common.

REFERENCES

1. "Factors Favoring the Persistence of a Relic Association of Eastern Hemlock in Indiana" by Rexford F. Daubenmire. *Butler University Botanical Studies* **2** (August, 1931), 29-32.
2. "Studies in Forest Ecology: I, Factors Concerned in Hemlock Reproduction in Indiana," by Ray C. Friesner and John E. Potzger. *Butler University Botanical Studies* **2** (November, 1932), 133-143.
3. "The Relation of Certain Ecological Factors to the Inhibition of Forest Floor Herbs Under Hemlock" by Rexford F. Daubenmire. *Butler University Botanical Studies* **1** (January, 1930), 61-76.
4. "A Study in Soil Moisture, Acidity, and Evaporation, in an Upland Woods at Turkey Run State Park," by Mary Fritsche Cundiff. *Butler University Botanical Studies* **9** (May, 1949), 108-123.
5. "The Mechanical Action of Crustaceous Lichens on Substrate of Shale, Schist, Gneiss, Limestone, and Obsidian," by E. J. Fry. *Annals of Botany* **41** (1927), 437-460.
6. "The Ecological Succession of Mosses, as Illustrated upon Isle Royale, Lake Superior," by W. S. Cooper. *Plant World* **15** (1912), 197-213.
7. *The Deciduous Forest of Eastern North America* by E. Lucy Braun. Discussion of Turkey Run State Park, 310-311. Blakiston, Philadelphia, 1950.
8. "Starved Rock State Park" by C. O. Sauer, G. H. Cady and H. C. Cowles. *Bulletin of the Geographic Society of Chicago* **6** (1918).
9. "Dynamics of Leaf Variation in the Sugar Maples" by Yves Desmarais. *Brittonia* **7** (October 6, 1952), 347-387.
10. *Story of the Plant Kingdom* by Merle C. Coulter. University of Chicago Press, Chicago, 1935.

6.

WATCHING THE
ISLANDS GO BY

or

Black Hawk's Perspective over the River

"And so-o," the great professor would conclude, stacking his notes, and pushing his spectacles down so that he could peer over them at his audience—

"And so, the natives can sit on the shore and watch the islands go by."

That was the closing line whenever Doctor Henry Cowles gave his River lecture in Physiographic Ecology.

It had been many years since I had thought of that last line. Then it came back suddenly one day.

We had pulled off on a shoulder of the road for a view of the statue of Black Hawk, chief of the Sacs, silently dividing, with his upright blanketed stature, the clamor of autumn oaks on the opposite bluffs, and thrusting deep into oak reflections in the Rock River. No wonder he had fought and burned and massacred to hold such wooded hills, such rivers, such prairie, against the white man's treaty that demanded all these lands east of the Mississippi.

No sooner were we out of the car than our two bird watchers were away up the shore, murmuring something about "the waders."

The sketcher was off in the other direction, holding her card with the peep-hole in it, and squinting selectively at the opposite bluffs, and Black Hawk, the river, the little boy who was fishing, and at the island.

The boy's rubbery fingers needed help in coping with the plump night crawler; and his mother and father were still eating lunch and listening to the radio in their car. I put the worm on the hook.

"You fish, too," he invited. So I took his father's pole from the bank and gutted another worm. It was pleasant there on the bank with the autumn sun on our backs.

A shout was whispered from upstream, as only bird watchers and head librarians can whisper a shout. No pointing; that was taboo in their ritual.

"Blue goose—on end of island!"

I saw him there, on the blunt, upstream end of the island, a lonely-looking individual, especially for October, when geese are seen in great congregations.

"Male, immature," breathed the first watcher from behind the gleam of binoculars.

"Juvenal plumage," exhaled the other watcher.

But just then the blue goose, male, immature, hurtled off precipitously. And where he had walked, an elm tree was lying down, in a tired sort of way, on one elbow first and then with its head in the river.

The water must have been undercutting that elm for a long time, and the straw that broke the camel's back apparently was laid on before our very eyes, even though the river looked so smooth.

The last yellow and brown leaves of the elm were dipped into the water. Many floated free. We watched them go.

They followed the long shoreline of the island. A few were caught in a tangle of low branches along the margin; some went on down the river.

But most of them gathered on the long tapering downstream tip of the island. There they stayed, bright among three green glass bottles that lay in a row, stem end upstream, along the side of that gritty tip.

That was the moment when I suddenly heard again that last line about watching the islands go by, and realized that I was seeing one in motion.

The elm leaves showed plainly enough how the substance of the island was traveling, how it was removed from the upstream end and deposited on the downstream tip. The green bottles were evidence that the island was growing by new deposits from the river.

The story of an island should, obviously, be read from the downstream tip, where there is perennial renewal, to the upstream end, where the chapter ends. Just exactly what was the succession of plant life out there, reading from low tapered bow to high blunt stern?

Just back of the bare tip, we could see a low dark-green patch. What was that? Back of it was a wine-colored drift. What was that? At this point the bird glasses came in handy. The dark-green patch proved to be rushes; and the wine-colored mass, lamb's-quarters.

How do rushes and lamb's-quarters arrive on an island? Both have minute seeds, without wings or other traveling devices.

A killdeer, coasting to a landing on the bare tip of the island, suggested a solution of the riddle. Lamb's-quarter seeds are known to be capable of lying dormant in mud for years. A killdeer might have landed in such mud, and carried seeds on his feet to this place.

Back of the lamb's-quarters was a tangled mass. In it we could detect milkweed, goldenrod, and thistles. The little fisherman's line had accumulated a mass of milkweed seeds. When it was time for a new worm, I plucked off one of the seeds to inspect it.

Here was a parachute for flight, and something more. It looked as if the seed were wearing a life preserver, a ring of corky material that might enable it to float. The seeds were coming down the river like boats under full sail. Many of the parachutes had become detached from their cargo and were floating free, but enough were complete. It was plain that milkweed might have arrived on the island either by air or by water.

Behind the tangle of milkweed, goldenrod, thistles, and other airborne pioneers, was a tall jungle of giant ragweeds. Beyond the ragweeds came the first of the woody plants. These were willows—all willows, in a dense, weedy mass of shrubby growth, six to ten feet high.

That would be sand-bar willow, *Salix interior*, chief pioneer of the soggy frontiers—sand bars, mud banks, downstream tips of islands. Wherever a river, slackening its speed, drops its load, the sand-bar willow is likely to be the first woody-stemmed opportunist to appropriate the new-made land. The thicket that we were observing was probably composed of only a few individuals, perhaps not more than one, sending up many trunks from wide-spreading roots and creeping stems.

Willows have two means of transport to an island. The seeds are air-borne, and the twigs have a habit of snapping off at the base and floating downstream, broad end first (as those three green glass bottles must have done), and becoming lodged in debris along the shore, where they take root. A willow's tendency to root from a twig is easily understood by anyone who has seen a springtime bunch of pussy willows develop roots in the water.

Behind the sand-bar willows, upstream, were bigger willows, actual trees. Beyond those were taller, wider, older willows. Mingled with the willows were silver maples, *Acer saccharinum*, showing the same many-trunked broad shape that seems to belong to the riverside fraternity always, and to the upland aristocracy not at all.

A few cottonwoods, those cosmopolitan pioneers of both wet and dry situations, were present.

There were a few box-elders and ashes, too. Those may have arrived on the wind, but I have seen their seeds often, in winter, skating over the ice, so they may conceivably have skated to the island.

Along the side of the island, near the upstream end, was a single

104

hawthorn tree. How does a hawthorn arrive on an island? Probably this seed arrived in the intestine of a bird. If so, the parent tree could not have been too far away on the mainland, since a bird's digestion is rapid. Probably, out of the many hawthorn seeds that were brought thus, this particular one throve because it happened to be on the drier part of the island, in the sun, and in the hawthorn's usual habitat, the forest margin.

The upstream end of the island was entirely dominated by elms. Here again was a tree that used air transportation for pollen and seeds; one that had a wide-spreading top, and that could thrive with wet feet—but not such wet feet as the willow can tolerate.

The elms were the final chapter, with the elm that toppled over into the river as the final sentence and the depositing of the upstream substance onto the tapering downstream tip, as the first sentence of the next chapter.

Along the river road from Rockford to Grand Detour we listed, with the aid of bird glasses, the vegetation on each island in the Rock River. The succession from tip to butt end was the same on island after island. Some of the smaller islands did not attain the elm stage before their upper end was shifted to their lower end. Islands in a wide, shallow stretch of the river, and islands in the still water above a dam showed both ends tapered.

As we drove south along the river, we tried to visualize the sort of trip that our island below the Black Hawk statue might take, if there were no dams, no rush of tributary waters to alter its course, nothing but placid, steady advance.

Before many miles some new passengers would certainly come aboard. Sycamore would be first, rearing the layered patches of its bark and the bleached antlers of its boughs high above the upstream end, perhaps having time to form a huge hollow trunk for opossums and racoons to inhabit, before it would inevitably be toppled off into the river.

Somewhere between southern Illinois and Missouri banks, the catalpa and the river birch would quietly take passage. Farther down the river the sweet gum would unobtrusively come aboard.

Then some of the passengers would disembark. Silver maple, and catalpa, and elm, would leave before the end of the trip; but the sand-bar willow would probably ride the prow the whole way.

Presently bald cypress would raise its bony knees along the margin; there would be scrub palmetto, and draperies of Spanish moss, and great white egrets nesting.

The final passengers would have to endure, not only excessive moisture, but also the bitterness of salt spray in their faces. The live oak seems able to tolerate both conditions, and Black Hawk's island might conceivably end its final chapter under the wide-spreading branches of fine live oaks.

There was one moment in our "islanding" when we felt a sudden kinship with the illustrious men out of the past who have devoted study to islands. That was the moment when we discovered our island's "mystery." Each renowned island the world over has seemed to present a mystery—or, at least, a problem.

On Easter Island, in the South Pacific, it was a matter of 550 statues, cyclopean masonry platforms, stone houses, that formed the "unsolved mystery of the Pacific."

On Crete it was the beginning and end of the advanced Minoan culture that formed the mystery.

On New Zealand it was the presence of wingless birds.

On Australia it was the lack of mammals, and the fact that marsupials were filling each ecological niche.

On Galápagos, it was the giant reptiles that interested Darwin first and Beebe later; and the finches that had developed to fill each ecological niche that would usually have been filled by some other kind of bird.

On Krakatoa it was the return of vegetation after the great volcanic eruption.

On our island in the Rock River, it was the summer home of a squirrel, high in the tips of an elm tree.

Why should he have built there where there was not a single nut tree? Did he swim back to shore every time he remembered the taste of acorns? Did he come swimming home again, with his

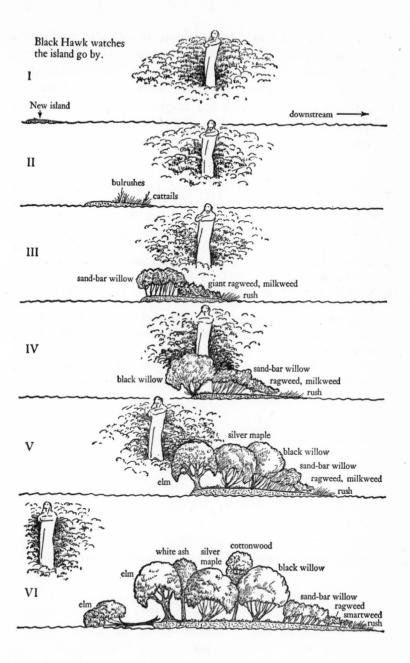

Black Hawk watches
the island go by.

I

New island

downstream ⟶

II

bulrushes

cattails

III

sand-bar willow

giant ragweed, milkweed

rush

IV

black willow

sand-bar willow

ragweed, milkweed

rush

V

silver maple

black willow

sand-bar willow

ragweed, milkweed

rush

elm

VI

white ash   silver
maple

cottonwood

black willow

elm

sand-bar willow

ragweed

smartweed

rush

elm

cheeks bulging like two shopping bags? It was a squirrel's nest, plainly enough. It showed clearly in the bright rays of the setting sun. The whole island, and Black Hawk, were ruddy with sunset.

The little boy had caught a bullhead, and his father had come to admire it. The bird watchers had caught a glimpse of a spotted sandpiper, fall adult.

So we left Black Hawk to watch the islands go by.

REFERENCES

1. *Journal of Researches into the Natural History & Geology of the Countries Visited During the Voyage Round the World of H.M.S. 'Beagle' Under Command of Captain Fitz Roy, R.N.*, by Charles Darwin. John Murray, London, 1912 (original ed. 1845).
2. *Galápagos, World's End* by William Beebe. Putnam, New York, 1924.
3. "Trees for the Aleutians" by David Bruce and Arnold Court. *Geographical Review*, (July, 1945), New York.
4. "Darwin's Finches" by David Lack. *Scientific American* **188** (April, 1953), 66-74.
5. "Small Mammal Populations on the Islands of Basswood Lake, Minnesota," by Beer, Lubens, and Olson. *Ecology* **35** (October, 1954), 347-445.
6. "The Wreck of the Belle Memphis" by Virginia Eifert. *The Living Museum*, The Illinois State Museum. Springfield, Illinois.

7.

CAMP SITES, FIRES, AND CUD-CHEWERS

or

*How the Upland Forest Changes from
Illinois to Wisconsin*

RUMINANTS and fires played a part in our trip from the very start
before we had even reached the place in Wisconsin where we were
to pick up our canoe. Fires long dead, and ruminants of two kinds,
shaped our first lunch stop.

That was in northern Illinois.

A splendid piece of woodland, four-layered, had red oak and white
oak forming the canopy, with ironwood, young sugar maples,
spikenard, and bloodroot beneath. We considered lunching there,
but we were discouraged, partly by signs, partly by mosquitoes,
but most of all by an efficient fence. By excluding ruminants, this
was responsible for preserving the four-layered aspect.

We stopped instead in an oak opening, where old bur oaks stood
widely spaced, with a few hawthorns, a blackberry patch, and
grass beneath.

If buffalo had not grazed out there in the prairie beyond these woods; if Indians had not hunted the buffalo with prairie fires; if the prairie fires had not beaten against the edge of the forest; if the bur oak had not worn a corky bark that kept it from being eliminated along with the thinner-barked trees; if a farmer who came after the Indians had not turned his cows into this oak opening to graze; and if hawthorns had not worn stout thorns that kept them from being grazed by the cows, then we should not have been lunching in a parklike area such as this, and listening to a brown thrasher singing in a hawthorn tree.

Hawthorns and blackberries under bur oaks mark a grazed forest

After lunch we walked through the oak opening to the pasture where the cows were grazing. There, invading the bluegrass and redtop that had replaced big bluestem and Indian grass under the influence of plows and cows, were many strangely shaped specimens —cow-pruned hawthorns. We could see every stage in that mute drama of a midwestern pasture.

The earliest stage was hardest to find. They were not as tall as the mullein stalks, those tiny hawthorns. We found one that a cow had just been nibbling. It was not more than four years old and seemed to be having a struggle for existence. It would probably have been devoured completely had it not had a few thorns.

Nearby was an older specimen, denser, thornier, with more years of intensive cow-pruning in its history. The perfect cone shape looked almost artificial.

Beside it stood one of a little later stage, wider, higher, but just as dense and trim. Evidently it had managed to do a little growing each year in spite of the intensive clipping of tender tips.

Not far away grew a hawthorn that seemed to be making the first triumphant gesture in this sequence. It had slowly grown just wide enough so that the cows could no longer quite reach the tip of the

Pasture hawthorn
1. tender tips

Mullein is felt-covered

Pasture hawthorn
2. pruning

Thistle is prickly

Pasture hawthorn
3. slow growth in spite of pruning

Vervain is bitter

cone. That was the turning point. Suddenly it was able to pour its growth upward, uninhibited.

Then came the hourglass stage. Several in that stage stood around the pasture, trimmed by cows, as far in, and just as far up, as they could reach.

Up above the cows' reach the branches began to spread horizontally, in the characteristic way of the hawthorn.

111

Pasture hawthorn
4. top shoots inaccessible

Pasture hawthorn
5. hour-glass shape

Pasture hawthorn
6. spreading branches

Gradually the wide-spreading branches shaded out the old cone at the base of the trunk. A few broad trees still wore a ring of dead sprouts around their feet—all that remained of the barbed-wire entanglement that made their development possible.

This cow-pruned hawthorn story may have a prelude, also with the cow as the chief factor. Some sort of prelude is needed to explain the survival of the seedling tree during its first two or three years, because thorns on seedlings are much too tender to repel a grazer. I can eat them, and have, as an experiment.

One summer the Morton Arboretum, where I work, was enlarged to include a considerable piece of land, mostly pastured, with many hawthorns.

While helping to make a plant count there (made immediately after the cows were taken out, so that we can record the changes during the coming years), I began to suspect that a cow-pruned hawthorn may owe its existence, as well as its shape, to a cow. The fastidiousness of a cow may be an ecological factor.

This is the way it apparently happened in this field:

1. A cow deposited dung.

2. No cow ate close to that patch in the following season. The cow dung became ringed with ragweed. Ragweed has good seeds for birds. A bird that came to eat had previously eaten a hawthorn fruit.

3. A little hawthorn started to grow in this sanctuary, well-protected, well-fertilized.

4. The cows did not eat close in the second year either. Yarrow and other weeds replaced most of the ragweed. The tiny seedling had sun, shelter, room, organic fertilizer, mulch.

113

5. The cows seemed not to reach the seedling in the third year. The twigs had a chance to harden their wood and *stiffen their thorns*.

6. The cows seem to have overcome their fastidiousness at about the fourth year. Then the little tree was sharply pruned of all its tender tips, but not exterminated. (Some of the patches had prairie roses in them. A few had wild crab apples. A few had slippery elms, but those had no thorns to stiffen.)

We ate our supper beside Pleasant Lake, in southern Wisconsin, on an oak ridge between two kettle holes (as we call the bowl-shaped hollows formed where great chunks of ice were left behind by the glacier). Under these oaks there was grass, as there had been at our lunch stop in Illinois, and blackberries, too, but no hawthorns. Filling the same ecological niche that the hawthorn had filled under those bur oaks of northern Illinois was another tree that, like the hawthorn, was bird-distributed, and prickly, too. This was the red cedar, *Juniperus virginiana*.

All around the lake, on the many hills of that kettle-moraine country, there were red cedars among the oaks. Those hills had been grazed for many years before the farmers started selling off the lake-front plots to summer people. There were different shapes of red cedars, telling something about the different times at which plots had been sold and fenced off from cows.

Around the first cottages on the lake, fenced off more than fifty years ago, the few remaining cedars were a spindly, thin, brownish lot. The growing shade of both tall canopy trees and smaller understory trees had been too much for them.

On our own piece of land, where the cows were fenced out twenty-seven years ago, there were some shapely compact trees, big

114

ones, that had attained a good size in the sunny pasture openings. There were many smaller, spindly specimens, that were being over-topped by twenty-six-year-old oaks. Directly under the branches of several oaks there was a thick stand of small cedars, perhaps a record of a flock of cedar waxwings that perched there after feeding on cedar berries.

Across the lake, where sheep were still pastured, the hills looked parklike, manicured, with short-clipped grass, and with the cedars trimmed as far up as sheep can nibble, standing—with their fore-feet braced against the trunk.

oaks red cedar

Red cedars took the place of haw-thorns in grazed woods

mullein

blackberry

Any occasional hawthorn that I have found around this lake has been puny, distorted, and dying, with orange spots on its sparse foliage. These orange spots are the mark of the cedar-apple rust. In the fall, each spot develops white beards on the underside of the leaf. These put out spores. Some of them, wind-borne, make a landing on a red cedar. There they slowly develop into cedar apples. By the second spring, these brown "apples" are about an inch in diameter. Then they put out beards, and become orange and gelatin-ous. At that time their spores are taking to the wind. Some of them land on a hawthorn. The drastic loss of leaf surface suffered as a result, weakens and eventually kills the hawthorn. Because these two trees that may fill the same ecological niche are alternate hosts to this cedar-rust, one does not find them hobnobbing in a grazed woodland.

As we ate our supper there on the ridge between the kettle holes, it was so warm that we discussed going over to the farmer's field, to see if it was true that one could hear the corn growing on warm nights. But it was too warm for any effort, and we fell to talking, instead, about the camp sites we hoped to find. We visualized tall pines and hemlocks, close-ranked, with a deep pile of needles under our sleeping bags, and enough balsam fir for stuffing our pillows.

What we were hoping for was the forest that greeted the early settlers, with marching miles of potential ship masts, beams, clear-grained framing and siding. Such a forest in Wisconsin records two conditions: sandy soil, and/or fires. It is not a self-replacing forest. Should enough time elapse without fires, even the sandiest of soils would probably be clothed with a cover of hemlock, beech, sugar maple, and yellow birch. That canopy will have a young forest of the same trees rising up through its shade. The forest will then have arrived at the self-replacing stage. Every ecological niche will be filled, with no room available to outsiders—unless some force such as man, or fire, or wind, opens a place, and lets the sun in again for a while.

When we hoped for balsam fir to fill our pillows, even while we slept on pine needles between uniform tapering columns, we were depending on the habit forests have of interlacing long fingers with neighboring forests. Balsam fir found here could only be a finger poking south from the boreal forest of spruce and balsam fir.

Many years previously, I had botanized in some imposing stands of white pine, red pine, and hemlock, in the Lake Superior region. Appallingly often, when we talked to local people, they told us that the forest we admired was to be cut during the next year. The urgency at that time was World War I.

During succeeding years, we made two canoe trips into this area. Twice we had the good fortune, my high-school son and I, to camp under tall stands of pine and hemlock; once on an island in Crab Lake, and once on a high bank overlooking Presque Isle Lake, where the hemlocks were memorable. That was the place where we heard wolves howl one night; and where the arborvitae

116

fringing the shores had been neatly trimmed to the height that deer could reach from the frozen lake. At that time I had failed to see the connection between the wolves and the arborvitae.

World War II, and the building boom that followed, had incited more cutting of forests.

That we might succeed in camping, for even one night, in the forest of my memories, was almost too much to hope for. But I hoped for it, nevertheless, because I wanted to show it to my daughter before it should have disappeared utterly.

In the early morning we hoisted the canoe on to the top of the car, and started north. We had only five days for our canoe trip, and one of those days must be devoted to transporting the canoe from Pleasant Lake to White Sand Lake in the Northern Highlands Forest. Another must be spent in transporting the canoe back to Pleasant Lake. That left us with four nights out, with four different camp sites along the circular route we had laid out on the map.

As we drove north we read the succession of records that rain and sun and soil and man have written across the face of Wisconsin. We were not reading the margins of the highways, because we realized that highway margins are dominated by European plants. Nor were we reading the river valleys. We knew that southern vegetation pokes its long fingers northward up the river valleys. Nor did we read the bogs that we passed, because those held a relict vegetation, left behind by the glacier's invasion. What we did read was the upland of Wisconsin. We were watching eagerly for indications that we were approaching our visualized camp site.

The first change was in the barns. The roadsides were still dominated by bouncing Bet and chicory, and the small towns by hollyhocks, when the big dairy barns, with their plump silos, gave way, somewhat abruptly, to a different type of barn, flimsier-looking, with slits in its vertical siding. Tobacco barns they were. The tobacco, that thrives on cold nights, made dark-green patches here and there in the landscape pattern. The corn, that thrives on warm nights, was no longer dominating the scenery.

The next indication of change was read on signs along the roadsides, hung out near the mailboxes. The signs said, "Maple Sugar For Sale. Maple Syrup for Sale." And when we stopped at a roadside stand we bought not only maple sugar, but also basswood honey.

We ate our lunch late, but we ate it on a high hill overlooking slopes covered with maple and basswood forest. We had planned to eat breakfast in one type of forest, lunch in another, and supper in still another. So far we were running on schedule.

As we started north again we noticed that the dairy barns had taken on a new appearance. Many of them had the upper part overhanging the first story on one side, with arched openings under the overhang. That provision for shelter for cattle spoke of winters that were growing harder.

And presently the trees that have become adjusted to longer winters made their appearance. We began to see small groves of evergreens here and there, but we did not find ourselves passing smoothly into the evergreen forest. Instead, for mile after mile, there was a scrubby growth of birch, aspen, and jack pine.

These are the "pioneers," with special qualifications for clothing the burned-over and cut-over areas and for preparing the way for the eventual forest, and, simultaneously, for their own extermination.

Here were jack pines by the million. Nothing stately about them; nothing to inspire the galaxy of poems that white pines have engendered, but with one distinctive character, their cones. These stay closed for a long time, sometimes not opening until touched by the heat of a forest fire, with the result that the fire may automatically help to reforest the area that it is deforesting.

Here, too, were birches and aspens, rising three-fold, or five-fold, from the cut or burned stumps. This root-sprouting habit, and the presence of abundant winged seeds, are important features of these pioneers. The feature that limits the tenancy of pioneers is their inability to tolerate shade.

As we continued northward there was an occasional narrow spire of a balsam fir or white spruce. By the time these began to appear, the big dairy barns had definitely disappeared.

At Stevens Point we unconsciously put on a burst of speed. That was because of a sudden fear that all the woods would be gone before we reached our first camp site—there were such great piles of pine logs along the Wisconsin River. Many of the piles were of small stuff—pulpwood. But several piles were of sizable logs.

We were within the limits of the pine-hemlock forest. On the courthouse lawn in Portage we saw a section of a huge white pine, with a bronze plate, explaining that this was a piece of one of the very last of the Big Pines of Wisconsin. In Wausau there was another section, with another bronze tablet.

We drove along, visualizing the endless upright battalions that had met the eyes of the pioneers, the forest described by Increase Lapham in 1852(1), by T. C. Chamberlain in 1877(2), and by C. S. Sargent in 1884(3). We couldn't help wishing that Paul Bunyan and his blue ox, famed in lumber-camp tales, had been a little less muscular.

We passed the gadget outcrops of the tourist shopping towns at Minocqua and Woodruff, and then left the highway at last, to follow a dirt road to White Sand Lake.

There we found a memorable camp site. Before sliding the canoe into the lake we ate wintergreen and a handful of blueberries as a sort of ritual; and we squeezed and smelled a handful of balsam-fir needles, and a leaf of Labrador tea. Then we cooked our supper on a high spot among jack pines and birches that told of lumbering and fire.

Before it grew quite dark we had time to visit the dark little stream that hurtled along among tamarack trees and alders, and curved around our camp site to pour its mahogany waters into the lake.

We spread our sleeping bags on the sandy shore under a few tall white pines and red pines. Among the pines a few narrow spires of balsam fir and white spruce were outposts of the boreal forest to the north; two small red oaks, northern extensions of the forest to the south. A small sugar maple represented the forest of maple, beech, yellow birch, and hemlock that is destined to clothe this site when sandy soil and man and fire shall cease to dominate.

Folding fans of northern lights, and the voices of a loon and two owls, made sleep unprofitable. I lay and wondered about the two trees that were missing from this assemblage.

There should have been hemlock among the pines; and there should have been arborvitae along the margin of the brook; and, along with the rich undergrowth of wintergreen, clintonia, prince's

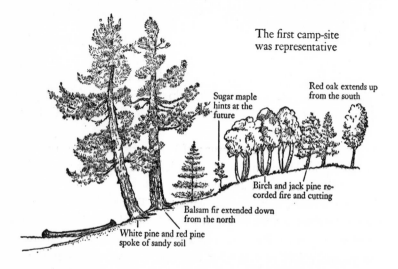

The first camp-site was representative

Red oak extends up from the south

Sugar maple hints at the future

Birch and jack pine recorded fire and cutting

Balsam fir extended down from the north

White pine and red pine spoke of sandy soil

pine, trailing arbutus, and club mosses, there should have been yew. Where were the hemlocks, the arborvitae, the yew?

Evidently we had not yet achieved our goal of a camp site in the forest that first challenged Paul Bunyan. But, none the less, it was a good first camp site, offering a sampling of all the situations we might expect to encounter.

In the morning we crossed White Sand Lake into White Sand River. For many hours we twisted and turned and ducked among alder, tamarack, and black spruce, wading three times to push the canoe over beaver dams.

Then White Sand River flowed into the swift current of the

clean, sand-bottomed Manitowish, and we rode the current into Boulder Lake.

Scowling, growling skies drove all thought of a pine forest out of our minds, and we made a hurried camp among birches, harebells, and bracken fern—not much of anything else in the way of vegetation. The birches were many-trunked, most of them, recording a fire that had followed the obvious lumbering.

The wet margin of our point had the usual wet-edge material—hazelnut, alder, *Spiraea alba*—but no arborvitae.

The knob back of the point had a few red pines, and one or two white pines, but no hemlock, no yew.

The second camp-site recorded lumbering and fire

birches

hazel and alder   bracken

Across the bay, two does and a fawn came down to the water. They, like the howling wolves that my son and I had heard on a previous trip, were clues that we failed to interpret until later.

Next day, after a portage past the rapids, and a pause to fish the white water, there were long hours on the clean Manitowish, with two imposing beaver dams to cross, and with the discovery that one of the best possible ways to see wild life is to float with the current down a lonely river.

A mink swam along beside us, close to shore, dodging under roots, and bobbing up again. We lost his company because the current carried us faster than he swam. A porcupine thrust out a piggy snout and beady eyes between rushes at the stream's edge. A merganser and twelve young swam sedately ahead of us, and then all silently submerged as we gained on them. A buck scooped up mouthfuls of duckweed, slobbered noisily. On a steep bank lay many shells of turtle eggs, probably the remains of a buried nest rifled by skunks.

Then the current faded as the river merged into the unnatural flowage area with its drowned trees and wildly gesturing upturned roots marking water held by a recent dam. We were glad to be out of that, and into Island Lake, heading for a camp site that the Boy Scouts who had helped us portage at the rapids had told us about.

From a distance, as we approached, it seemed as if we had reached our goal. Certainly we were headed toward a grove of tall pines. But, as we beached our canoe, and climbed up over the bluff, we realized that this was not virgin forest.

The third camp-site recorded thinning, camping

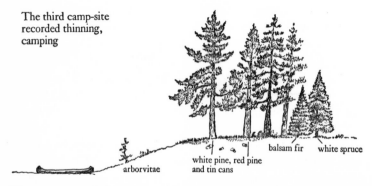

arborvitae

white pine, red pine and tin cans

balsam fir   white spruce

The trees stood far apart, with a parklike aspect, and there was grass beneath them, and—tin cans. The grass and the tin cans explained each other. The grass came after the forest had been thinned by cutting, letting in the sun. That was long ago. These pines had obviously had plenty of elbow-room during most of their lives. The tin cans were there because many large-group canoe trips from the camps on these lakes had found this open site ideal for an overnight stop; and because the animals of the forest had found it easy and rewarding to dig up the buried cans.

The trees were predominantly red pine and white pine, with a few balsam firs and a few white spruces. Still, there was no hemlock, no yew.

There was, to be sure, one single specimen of arborvitae down beside the lake. But it had scarcely any foliage, and looked as if it could hardly last another season.

Next morning we crossed Island Lake, and the motor-churned waters of Spider Lake, and Manitowish Lake, and then started paddling a water path through wild-rice fields.

All afternoon we were in the wild-rice fields, on Rice Lake, Alder Lake, and then on the Trout River, with a pause to eat handfuls of serviceberries where the stream swung close to a bluff, while an osprey ogled us from a high bare tree.

After that approach to the bank, the avenue of open water stayed far from either shore for a long time, so long that we were tired enough to give up all thought of one final camp site in a pine-hemlock forest.

Then suddenly the open path swung over, close to a high bank. We had to beach the canoe and climb the high sandy bluff to see whether there had been a camp fire there. There had been, a small one, with no tin cans.

But it was a long time before we got around to unloading our duffel. There was too much to see.

There were acres of tall close-ranked white pines and red pines. Such a stand of even-aged pines usually records a fire, followed by a good seed year.

But among and under the pines were hemlock trees, smaller than the pines. And, on the forest floor, along with the wintergreen, and pipsissewa, linnaea, lycopodiums, coral mushrooms, and partridgeberry, there was yew.

Having found two of the missing members present, we sought a lower spot, back of the camp site, and there the third one, arborvitae, was thriving. We had evidently found our camp site in an intact piece of the Northwoods of memory.

Why was it intact?

We were standing on the bluff, under a hemlock, when I looked down and saw a cartridge shell half-hidden under partridgeberry. It offered the link that I needed.

123

I looked at the map. All afternoon we had been within the bounds of the Flambeau-Ojibway Indian Reservation. These Indians had no closed season on deer. They could shoot when they wanted to shoot.

I remembered that arborvitae is considered the number one deer browse in the winter, and hemlock second; and yew is another favorite. Then I remembered pictures of dead deer in the snow—pictures that Aldo Leopold(5) had shown one evening as he explained the mass starvation of deer in places where the deer population had become too dense to be supported on the natural deer fodder.

Our first three camp sites had been in areas where the deer were probably hungrily consuming every bit of available hemlock, arborvitae, and yew. The nature of the forest in such areas had been altered by man, who first eliminated the wolf, natural predator on

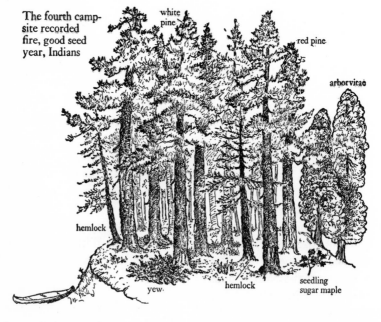

The fourth camp-site recorded fire, good seed year, Indians

white pine

red pine

arborvitae

hemlock

yew

hemlock

seedling sugar maple

deer, and then protected the does until they had reproduced them-selves out of browse.

Standing there, looking down at the cartridge shell, I remembered the camp site, several summers ago, where wolves had howled. There had been hemlock there, and abundant arborvitae.

Now that we had attained our desired camp site, it took us a long, long time to settle down to making camp. There was the glow of the low sun on red pine trunks to distract us; and there was the rich pattern of the forest floor with its embossing of waxed and polished leaves.

Above that rich carpet rose a few young sugar maples and yellow birch, indicating the eventual destiny of this site, when the shade-tolerant hardwoods and hemlock take over. There will probably be, here and there, a venerable white pine left behind, topping the others, but not reproducing itself in that denser shade—not unless there should be a windfall that would let the sun in again, or a fire.(7)

There were strange rectangular holes near the bases of many of the pines. About two inches wide by nine inches long by two inches deep they averaged, with square corners. Some were older and had become less angular as the tree healed the incision. Others were recent, with huge chips, an inch or two long, lying around.

It might have looked as if the last campers on this site had been equipped with sharp chisels and had gone berserk, unless one remembered the existence of the only bird capable of such carpentry—a bird of northern wilderness, the pileated woodpecker, seeking ants. When we finally caught a glimpse of the massive head and showy crest of this great bird we could understand the story that a forester in the Cascades had told us, about the way the Klamath Indians scalped the birds, keeping the upper half of the bill and the crest, and wearing them dangling, to use in the purchase of wives.

We did not find arborvitae in abundance. The site was too high. But next morning, when we took to the Trout River again, it suddenly became swirling rapids with thick gnomelike forest on both sides. Trees, leaning and old and dead, and young and green and upright, were hung with mosses and lichens, and continuously moist with the spray of the white water.

We finally waded, pushing the canoe, and saw that here was arborvitae in abundance, leaning out from both sides. We were out of the Indian reservation, but evidently not even a deer would walk those violent stony waters for his chosen food.

Suddenly we emerged into the calm of Trout Lake. We had only to cross the lake, walk to our car, bring it to the lake, and put the canoe on top. Then we started south, behind car licenses that said, "America's Dairyland," ruminating as we drove—on the ruminants.

REFERENCES

1. "Woods of Wisconsin" by Increase A. Lapham. *Transactions of Wisconsin State Agricultural Society*, (1852).
2. "Native Vegetation" by T. C. Chamberlain. *Geology of Wisconsin, Wisconsin Geological and Natural History Survey*, (1877).
3. *Report on the Forests of North America, Exclusive of Mexico*, by Charles Sprague Sargent. (U.S. Department of Interior, Census Office Report.) Government Printing Office, Washington, 1884.
4. "The Hemlock-White Pine-Northern Hardwoods Region of Eastern N. America," by G. E. Nichols. *Ecology* (July, 1955).
5. *A Sand County Almanac and Sketches Here and There* by Aldo Leopold. Oxford, New York, 1949.
6. "Watching Animals Eat" by Alfred G. Etter. *The Land* 11 (January, 1953).
7. "The Forests of Itasca in the Nineteenth Century as Related to Fire" by Stephen H. Spurr. *Ecology*, 35 (January, 1954), 21-25.

8.

PICNIC IN A GRITTY WIND

or

The Sand Dunes of Indiana

A SURE way to insight into the life of the Indiana dunes is to attempt to eat lunch there, on the beach, on a windy day in late October.

One has to give up, of course.

We had to give up one October day. And as we worked our way inland, across the dunes, in unhurried search for a more static, restful luncheon spot, we found ourselves reading the story of the dunes in a particularly intimate fashion—identifying ourselves with them, so to speak.

The facts and theories that forty years of intermittent botanizing in the dunes have taught me seemed, on that one day in the gritty wind, to become transmuted into reality.

Probably, in the "old days" when we waded at the edge of the lake, under Doctor Elliot Downing's direction(7), scooping up nets full of tiny creatures for examination, we were too soggy to have any empathy with a dune. Our viewpoint at that period might have been the viewpoint of a crayfish or a clam. Later, on the many

127

trips when with eager ears cocked forward, we followed in the quick footsteps of Doctor Cowles(1), we were still much too young and vigorous, and too enchanted with the new field of Ecology, to care about sun or wind, or sand between our teeth. Our viewpoint was that of pioneer plants, such as marram grass and wormwood and tough cottonwoods. And, some years later, when we meandered in the incandescent wake of Jens Jensen, Danish landscape man, and of Harriet Monroe of *Poetry Magazine*, our heads were too high in the clouds for us to be conscious of the assault of quartz grains. Our viewpoint then was akin to that of gulls and wheeling terns. And on a recent December a field trip through the dunes under the leadership of E. L. Palmer of Cornell and Edwin Way Teale, naturalist and author, our minds were too busy for our bodies to notice much. Our viewpoint here might be likened to that of inquisitive and acquisitive crows.

But when we came to the dunes on an October sketching trip, and wanted, before we started painting, to eat lunch, we were enough older to want peaceful shelter, and earthy enough to want our food without quartz sand. Our viewpoint had become that of the shaded and sheltered maidenhair fern, or of white trillium. Then the story of the dunes, reading from the shore of Lake Michigan inward, became revealed to us as the story of gradual preparation for maidenhair fern—and for elderly, hungry botanists.

As we started off eastward from Waverley Beach, where we had left our car, we walked on the hard wet sand at the water's edge. Out under the water we could just see the first sand bar, and we could remember the succession of sand bars that lay beyond, from the many summers when we had gone swimming from that beach.

Those sand bars were part of the material that Lake Michigan had gnawed off of its western shore, and was dumping there. That sand was destined to become dunes after the water handed it over to the wind to carry still further.

Back beyond the wet beach, where it was dry underfoot, we saw the sand-bar shape repeated in the ripples in the sand—but modeled there by wind instead of water.

New dunes were arriving
as sand bars

That shape—the long gentle slope on the windward side and the abrupt slope on the leeward side—was to become very familiar to our feet before we could eat lunch in a cool sheltered peace.

There was a battered Monarch butterfly in the lee of one ripple. But we needed more of a shield than that.

A more generous bit of shelter lay ahead of us.

A great beam had been rolled in by the waves—part of a boat, perhaps. In the shelter of its leeward side a mound of sand had accumulated. In that improbable situation two little plants were growing, both the same kind, a tough little annual called sea rocket, *Cakile americana*. It had to be an annual to survive on this part of the beach, which, though dry in the summer, is washed by winter waves. It had exactly the qualities that might be expected of a plant able to survive sun and wind and moving sand. It was dwarf, distorted, gray-green. I tasted it, and found the bitter, horse-radish pungency that belongs to so many plants of sun-beaten places. The whole plant had the fleshy smoothness that tells of water storage. We pulled up one of the plants, and revealed roots that were surprisingly long and bushy and moist.

The roots made us realize that the sea rocket had probably not really required the windbreak formed by the beam, or had needed it only during the first few days of its life.

A monarch butterfly lay
behind a sand ripple

129

But we needed more shelter than that, our entire expanse being above ground.

We moved on across the beach, toward a mound that would have caught the eye of any sketcher, however hungry.

The gentle rise was topped and held by a photogenic tuft of marram grass (*Ammophila breviligulata*), that was pencilling arcs in the sand that itself had accumulated.

Two pioneer plants grew behind a wooden beam

Here was the real pioneer of the dunes. The sea rocket's display of hardihood is ever destined to be wiped out at summer's end, but marram grass can perennially spread underground, enlarging its clump, catching and holding sand in its intricate network, and growing ever higher up through the mound of sand that it accumulates, until it forms a small dune. In fact, both this pioneer and its close relative of English dunes, *Ammophila arenaria*, show a decline in vigor when the sand surface is stabilized(11, 12).

Marram grass and wormwood held a small mound

"Enough shelter for lunch?" we wondered, and tried sitting on the leeward side of the long mound. We could hear sand grains being stopped by the grasses. But they were not all stopped, so we moved on.

Before we left we noticed something else that had benefited from

130

this shelter. It was a gray-green mound of wormwood (*Artemisia canadensis*). We nibbled at its famed bitterness, and thought of its sun-baked western relative, the sage-brush.

These two dune pioneers, marram grass and wormwood, both have greatly-extended and much-branched root systems, out of proportion to their tops.

We moved inland toward a higher mound.

It looked as if this mound might have been started by marram grass. It was easy to imagine that the wind might have deposited a seed of sand-dune willow on the leeward side of the marram-grass mound, and a bird might have brought a seed of sand cherry. At any rate, there was a thriving clump of sand-dune willow (*Salix*

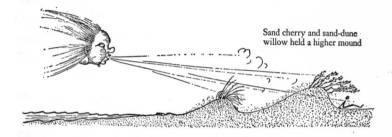

Sand cherry and sand-dune willow held a higher mound

syrticola) and a smaller one of sand cherry (*Prunus pumila*). The thick small leaves of the willow were eloquently different from the leaves of willows found in our river bottoms(3).

The willow-cherry dune was high enough but hardly long enough to give shelter to the five of us. The gritty wind came around the ends and found us.

Then we came across a strange thing in the level sand—two parallel rows of cottonwood seedlings. Evidently a wagon or a jeep had left ruts there, ruts that had cut down into the moist water table. Cottonwood seeds must have lodged in those ruts and prospered in their shelter and moisture, while other seeds landing on the open sand failed to make a start.

Those moist ruts were serving as miniature "pannes." Panne is the name ecologists give to an area from which the sand has been blown

131

out right down to the saturated sand of the water table. This wet sand does not blow away. It forms an important stage in the stabilizing of the dunes by vegetation.

Many plants germinate and get a good start in such pannes. But most of the plants are doomed. The sand inevitably fills in around them and chokes them out, *unless they can make adventitious roots.*

Cottonwoods *can* make adventitious roots. They can grow right up with the growing dune, because they can make new roots at consecutively higher levels as the sand builds up around their trunks. The cottonwoods that appear to be perched on top of a high dune actually have their original roots far below in a moist panne. Sometimes the whole story is revealed when a dune moves off and leaves a long-necked cottonwood behind.

We looked again at the little rows of cottonwoods at our feet, realizing that they might one day be the backbone of a tall dune, and hikers might walk up there among their tops and wonder why these trees grow in rows.

Cottonwood seeds had found wagon ruts

In fact, the cottonwoods at the top of the dune that lay just ahead of us looked suspiciously like the tops of buried trees. Perhaps they came from seeds that had started in ruts, or in footprints, perhaps in the print of a moccasin.

It was loose bare sand that we climbed through to reach the cottonwoods.

And they in turn were surrounded by loose, bare, and blowing sand. The lakeward side of their trunks was sandblasted to a high polish. We could watch the sand grains tumbling over the crest.

Plainly this first cottonwood dune was a moving dune, and the cottonwoods' hold was a temporary one only.

On the steep leeward slope and in the hollow at its base were a few pale herbs. There was bugseed, *Corispermum hyssopifolium,* a tough little annual like the sea rocket of the beach, with the rather plump narrow leaves and the pale-green color that seems to belong to sand pioneers. And there was a sparse colony of false Solomon's-seal, *Smilacina stellata.*

Here certainly was a height adequate to shelter us from the wind, but the leeward slope was too hot. We did not want to sit facing the sun. And the slope was too steep. We tended to slide like the sand grains.

So we sat down on a hump that had been built up by sand collected by a clump of sand-reed grass, *Calamovilfa longifolia,* and emptied our shoes—a futile operation.

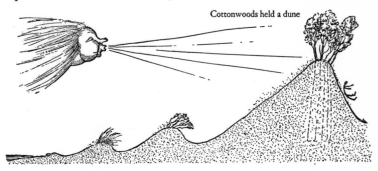

Cottonwoods held a dune

How dry it looked there at our feet, among those widely spaced plants! But when we kicked away the pale shifting sand of the surface, we uncovered wet-looking sand of deeper color. It felt moist and cool. Plainly the surface sand is stirred into an efficient dust mulch, as topsoil might be stirred by a farmer to hold the water beneath it.

Plants on a moving dune can drink deeply. The trouble is that wind and sun may drink faster from the leaves than roots can drink from the moisture in the sand. No wonder some of the leaves present a narrow vertical surface to the sun, a surface plump with water storage.

The next slope filled our shoes again, fast. It was bare and high. The sand went up and over faster than we did.

The ridge above us was ribbed with battered cottonwoods and lindens, sandblasted and sparse. We were glad to notice a dip in the top of the ridge.

As we headed toward this break, we could see a new darker green ahead. Then we realized that the break that was saving us a few steps and puffs was costing the vegetation, on the other side of the ridge, dearly.

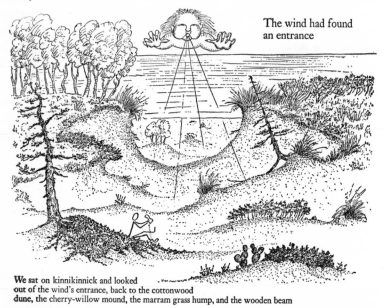

The wind had found an entrance

We sat on kinnikinnick and looked out of the wind's entrance, back to the cottonwood dune, the cherry-willow mound, the marram grass hump, and the wooden beam

This was plainly a "leak in the dike," where the wind had worked in one finger, then a whole hand, and now was using all its hands and feet and teeth.

We puffed up over the top, between a linden with a great saucer of common juniper at its feet, and a clump of sand cherry with a tuft of sand-reed grass at its feet.

Ahead of us lay a great bowl, holding many small mounds within its rim. The coloring was dramatic in comparison with the mousiness of the lakeward side of the ridge. Reds and oranges marked poison ivy and aromatic sumac, and the berries of kinnikinnick and bittersweet. Their brilliance was heightened by the stern deep green of evergreens.

We had come too late over the ridge. We could have eaten lunch there in great comfort, seated on an evergreen ground cover, in evergreen shade, sheltered from the wind by a ridge held static by evergreens, if we had come earlier—a year, or two or three years, earlier.

If the evergreens had been granted just a little longer respite, before the wind got its foot into a crack of the door, and *if* the cottonwood dune on the lakeward side had been given time to grow a little higher, and *if* that cottonwood dune had been sheltered by a younger cottonwood dune, perhaps accumulated by that row of seedlings in the wagon track, then this hollow might have become serenely clothed with a well-established forest.

As to the composition of that forest we can only speculate, on the basis of developments in other similar situations in the dunes. Certainly those developments have not always been the same(11).

Probably black oaks would have appeared among the evergreens. Their shade would gradually have eliminated evergreen seedlings. Under the black oaks would probably have been blueberries. This partnership, especially in the event of occasional fires, might have held the situation indefinitely. But, on the other hand, given surcease of fire, and good protection to windward, the black oak might have been replaced gradually by a forest of white oak, red oak, and ironwood, with sugar maples sprouting in its deepening shade.

But the "ifs" did not happen in time, and the wind *did* get its foot in the door. The vegetation was losing ground, actually losing ground. Common juniper was holding mounds of sand with its roots; but we could see where the wind was prying its fingers in under a jack pine. It would topple soon.

The others are doomed too—the few white pines, the carpets of kinnikinnick, and the scattered black oaks. As they go down, one by one, this will become another great dune blowout. Then winter will bring skiers who will appreciate the lack of obstruction; and summer will bring flower-arrangers who will appreciate the attenuated sandblasted root-tips clawing the blue sky, and will sigh over the possibilities for their picture windows.

Perhaps in time this blowout, like others in the dunes, will reveal remains out of the past. Some have revealed ancient pine forests buried long, long ago, perhaps on the beach of Lake Chicago. Others have revealed "kitchen middens" with their brittle baked and blackened stones. And, recently, there has been an interesting unearthing of mammal bones(5).

Jawbones and teeth made identification possible, not only of common mammals like rabibts, white-footed mice, and muskrats, but also of mammals long since gone from the dunes.

Of these earlier residents were found bones of white-tailed deer, elk, fisher, and bear. The bear remnant was "an incomplete skull with one complete maxillary tooth row and one incomplete one. From the amount of wear on the teeth it represents a young adult. Though considerably perished, the bone has little brown stain on it. It seems probable this material is more than 100 years old. It was found under a fallen dead tree of a forest that had been smothered by an advancing line of dune and is now nearly uncovered. The skull parts were recovered on two different trips, but fit together, indicating but one animal was involved"(5).

On a collecting trip to one blowout in the Dunes State Park, in 1951, it is reported(5) that four people searching for two hours found jaws and teeth of one mole, one chipmunk, one fox squirrel, four white-footed mice, two meadow mice, one muskrat, one porcupine, one cottontail, three or four Virginia, or white-tailed deer.

But our blowout was not yet ready to reveal the past. The evergreens were still holding their own fairly well. And this was one of their most buffeted days. That was why we decided not to eat lunch there, but only to empty our shoes again.

But we were careful about choosing a place to sit, because there was cactus in the blowout. It seemed to be on south-facing sides of the mounds. So we chose a north-facing side, and sat on kinnikinnick(4) at the base of a jack pine.

Where else in America could one sit amid dark green that is

wont to hobnob with ptarmigan and Eskimo and midnight sun, and look down upon the pale green that is the familiar of horned toads and Joshua trees and Navajos?

But the unlike appearances of these two plants speak of problems that are surprisingly alike. The jack pine in its arctic homeland has to survive the thirsty winter sun. The cactus, in its desert homeland, has to survive the thirsty summer sun. There is plenty of water around the roots of the northern jack pine, but water is not available when it is frozen. The cactus does not have water available either. One faces a physiological drought, the other faces a physical one.

The jack pine endures the winter drought of the far north because of all pines it has the best adapted leaf. The skin is so thick that it forms half the bulk of the leaf; there are strong protective palisade cells inside, and the stomata openings are sunk into the lower surface.

The cactus has leaves that are altered much more drastically than those of the jack pine. In fact, the leaves are hardly noticeable on the fleshy gray-green stem.

It is not surprising that these two strangers can both endure the drying wind and sun of the dunes. The surprising thing is that they should be in the dunes at all.

For the presence of the cactus, there is a choice of two explanations. It is one of a group of plants from the southwest that is found in the dunes, and along many sandy areas and dry, rocky ledges, between the dunes and the southwestern desert. The areas the plants inhabit are not too far apart for a normal migration by way of wind and birds; but, on the other hand, they may represent groups of plants left behind at the close of the "xerothermic," or hot-dry period, that followed the glacial period.

The jack pines of the dunes represent the most southerly extension of that species. Not only is it the most southerly but the colony in the dunes is an *island* of jack pines, separated by more than a hundred miles from the nearest outpost to the north. A disjunct community, such a situation is called.

This colony is a "relict" of the last glacial invasion. The evergreens that moved south before the oncoming glacier crept north again as the glacier retreated. The deciduous forest crowded them out of places that were fit for deciduous trees, and might, possibly, have already superseded them here had not the persistence of pines been favored by occasional fires and other disturbances(11).

The only places that the evergreens could hold on to, in the face of the northward march of the deciduous trees, were the difficult places, such as the edges of canyons (illustrated in Chapter 6, the Canyon story), the edges of acid bogs (Chapter 4, History Book with Flexible Cover) and the shifting sands of the dunes.

We reread the story

marram grass
cottonwood dune
sand cherry
linden
jack pine
juniper
white pine
linden
black oak
blowout

We got up from our rest among the evergreens, and started across the blowout.

I paused to squeeze a leaf of the aromatic sumac to enjoy its pungency. The leaves in the dunes were broader, I noticed, and not so thick-feeling as the leaves on the stunted specimen of aromatic sumac that I had been surprised to find once growing at my feet, far from any other plant, on a sterile gray expanse in the Badlands.

The dunes are certainly a good place for travelers to visit, to revive old friendships with plants met in diverse and distant places.

We continued across the restlessness and threat of the blowout, and climbed the next ridge. It was higher than any ridge we had climbed, and we could look back and reread the chapters up to this point.

At our feet lay the long blowout. Beyond it, we could see the gap where the wind had entered. And through the gap, we could see the cottonwood dune, then the sand-cherry dune, then the marram grass mound, and (with the aid of bird glasses) the beam that the lake had rolled ashore.

Then we turned our backs on the lake, and looked steeply down the leeward slope. We continued to look, for a long time. It rested our eyes.

Beneath us lay a peaceful deep hollow filled with familiar woodland. We had turned our backs on pioneers and relicts and invaders from the arid southwest. We had turned our backs on reduced leaf

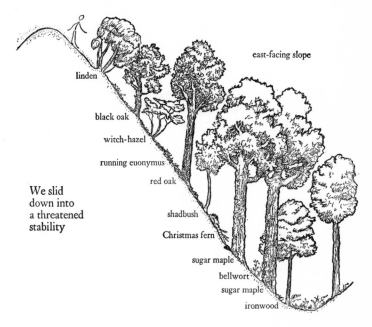

surfaces and aromatic oils and succulent leaves; also on milky juices and thick skins and leathery surfaces; and on pubescence, and other characters of plants that endure gritty wind and unrelenting sun.

We had turned our backs on the xerophytes, the dry-land plants, because we had found shelter from wind and sun.

We slid down among the mesophytes, the plants occupying the middle ground between dry and wet.

Here were lindens and sugar maples, bitternut hickory and red oak and ash. Underneath them were ironwood and shadbush and witch-hazel in bloom.

Underneath the ironwood and shadbush and witch-hazel were great patches of running euonymus and bellwort and Christmas fern.

Here was peace, and a look of stability and permanence. Certainly the gritty wind did not find its way into this hollow.

But the peace was doomed. As we stood at the foot of the slope that we had slid down, and looked back up to the top, we could see a thin mist of sand. A little sand was plainly beginning to tumble down that slope. The wind that had come in through a keyhole, and was playing havoc with the evergreen slope, had gained strength in its rush across the new blowout, and was beginning to move the dune that marked the end of the blowout.

Sugar maples, ironwoods, Christmas ferns, for all their look of peace, were marked for an enfolding doom. But some day they may be uncovered again, gaunt skeletons with writhing, sandblasted roots upturned.

But we knew a bank where ebony spleenwort and partridgeberry grew under great old white pines, beside a dark-brown creek. It was not far away. So we kept going, all nibbling hungrily at the twigs of the sassafras thicket we passed in a cut-over section.

We were soon crossing areas dominated by black oak above and blueberry below. According to a recent study (11), these are old dunes. It was long ago that they saw the waters of the lake, so long ago (according to the records of lime leaching downward through the sand) that some of them were dunes along the margin of an ancient lake of the glacial period. A specimen collected from dunes at Dolton, Illinois, was radio-carbon-dated by Willard F. Libby, as having died 3,496 (plus or minus 230) years ago.

Such well-established black oak and blueberry stands on old dunes may be a record of the xerothermic period, which would have favored their development. Once established, this partnership often forms a sort of "closed shop," acid, exclusive, holding land for a long time in its grip.

In some places the wind held sway again, and was prying out

established stands of plants. We saw a black oak that was plainly being dispossessed, even though it was far inland.

We skirted swamps fringed with sour gum, and rounded the end of a moving dune. Our feet seemed to remember the way to Little Fort Creek, and before long we were on the path that runs along and above the deep-brown creek, and at the base of a north-facing and sheltered slope.

A black oak was being dispossessed

Flowering dogwood spread its flat branches there. A few tulip trees grew nearby, and a few small beech trees. The beech trees were important. They were the western outposts of the eastern beech forests. Just so far they advance toward the prairie peninsula, and no farther.

Finally we came to a place where the steep slope beside the path was rich with the shining leaves and red fruit of partridge-berry and wintergreen. We found the patterned leaves of rattle-snake plantain, and patches of trailing arbutus. Great white pines curved up along the creek side of the path. All these plants represented a rich collection of relics from the glacial period.

Then we found the delicate little ebony spleenwort, and a big clump of maidenhair fern. There would have been masses of white trillium, if it had been spring.

It was the maidenhair fern that marked the end of the story that we had been reading. When we saw that, we knew that we had come as far from the conditions of the windy beach as it was possible to be, in the dunes.

We ate our lunch, seated in welcome shade, on pine needles. It tasted good, and no sand blew into it.

Here, finally, was a stabilized part of the dunes. Actually, we were well aware that a more stabilized part, where the cold spring and the mallows once had been, lay about 200 feet away—encased in concrete. This section of the dunes was now part of the Dunes State Park, and acres of parking space for the cars of swimmers, ball players, and picnickers had become necessary. I was careful not to catch a glimpse of that ominous stabilization lest it spoil my appetite. I could remember dunes on the north side of Chicago, dunes where our family would put up a tent on a summer day, under scrubby trees, in preparation for a day on the wild beach. (Botanizing today among childhood memories, I should identify the trees as black oaks.) There was an imposing high dune that I remember as a tragic site because my sister broke the handle of her ruffled pink silk parasol there as she used it to slow a headlong slide. (From this distance I should identify that as a moving dune.) The Edgewater Beach Hotel, many tall apartment buildings, acres of cement walks and highways now fill that flattened surface, and even the edge of the lake has been engineered far away to make a place for a newer highway.

We knew that what remained of our quiet path had not changed noticeably, except to widen a bit with use, in forty years. But we could see evidence that it could not remain stable much longer unless human erosion of the crest of the dune above the path were immediately halted.

After lunch we separated, to sketch all afternoon. Each one, turning away from shelter and security, followed the beaten path of the arts to subjects that evidenced insecurity, conflict, change, tension. One went back to the dispossessed black oak, another climbed high and wove a pattern of advancing waves of water and sand; another sought out exhumed sandblasted roots; another found a partly-undermined shack, standing askew, but with diapers on the clothes-line; another painted a bare sand wall poised high over living green.

No one drew the wind. But each redrew some selected detail from the masterpiece that the wind had drawn—and was still drawing.

REFERENCES

1. "The Ecological Relations of the Vegetation on the Sand Dunes of Lake Michigan" by Henry C. Cowles. *Botanical Gazette* **27** (1899).
2. *Plant Communities* by Warren G. Waterman. Northwestern University Publications, Chicago, 1928.
3. "The Comparative Anatomy of Certain Plants Common to Dunes and River Bottoms" by Clarence L. Holtzmann. Master's thesis (unpublished), University of Chicago, 1904.
4. "The Shrubs of Indiana in Their Local and General Distribution According to Physiographic Divisions" by Lettie Page Treftz. *Butler University Botanical Studies* **3** (April, 1935).
5. "Mammal Bones from Dunes South of Lake Michigan" by A. L. Reed and A. Stanley Reed. *The American Midland Naturalist* **46** (November, 1951), 649-659.
6. "The Ecology of the Spiders of Xeric Dunelands in the Chicago Area" by Donald C. Lowrie. *Bulletin of Chicago Academy of Sciences* **6** (March 16, 1942), 161-189.
7. *A Naturalist in the Great Lakes Region* by Elliot Rowland Downing. University of Chicago Press, Chicago, 1922.
8. *Flora of the Indiana Dunes* by Donald Culross Peattie. Chicago Field Museum of Natural History, Chicago, 1930.
9. *Downs and Dunes, Their Plant Life and Its Environment*, by Edward Salisbury. G. A. Bell and Sons, Ltd., London, 1952.
10. "The Disappearing Sleeping Bear Dune" by Frank C. Gates. *Ecology* **31** (July, 1950), 386-392.
11. "Vegetation Substrate Relations in Lake Michigan Dune Development" by Jerry Olson. Doctorate thesis (unpublished), University of Chicago, 1953.
12. *Plant Ecology and the School* by Arthur George Tansley and E. Price Evans. "Sand Dunes and Shingle Beach," 79-82. George Allen and Unwin, Ltd., London, 1946.

9.

RUNNING AWAY
FROM SPRING

or

Plains to Timber Line in the Rockies

RIDING the ski tow at Berthoud Pass, in March, is fun for anyone.

Whether it is more fun for the supple and besweatered, who ride up in order to come winging down, or for the slightly brittle, who ride up just for the ride, is debatable.

Anyhow, we were glad indeed to be riding up in the company of glinting skis and gay voices (and only a few set jaws, and perhaps a leg or two that might, by nightfall, need to be set) and just a little glad that our brittleness and years excused us from speeding down in that exuberant company.

"Spring! It's O. K. with me if it never comes," the young voice floated up from the chair behind mine.

It certainly looked from where we sat as if that young skier might have her wish. With every soundless, effortless foot of that soaring rise we were retreating farther back into winter, running farther away from spring.

But that was what we had been doing all day, ever since we left the foothills by car, to drive up to the foot of the ski lift.

Down there in the foothills, (to start the story of our day at its beginning) the pasque flowers had definitely said it was spring. They said it in several different ways: by wearing the Easter finery that befits their names, while pessimistically keeping on their silk-wool underwear; by displaying the pattern of the primitive Buttercup family (see Chapter 1) and reminding us that spring is a time of primitive floral patterns; by blooming close to the earth, where competition for sunlight would be much too great after the season advances; and by being soft to the touch, with a softness that would be much too vulnerable in the parched summer of the east face of the Rockies.

In the foothills the pasque flower said it was Spring

The rest of the foothills population offered only a few hints of spring. The south-facing grazed slopes wore snow only in the form of neatly tapered streaks—a streak to the north of every yucca and juniper and mountain mahogany. In the open groves of ponderosa pine, the snow blanket had become so patchy that dark masses of kinnikinnick showed through, and squaw currant bushes, and rusty clumps of mahonia. There were tight knobs of flower buds hidden among the ruddy leaves of the mahonia.

The river bottoms in the foothills said it was spring, but river bottoms are addicted to misstatements (if failure to agree with the stated opinion of the mass is a misstatement). River bottoms everywhere have a way of extending a finger of one type of vegetation into the mass of another type. Into the Foothills zone (usually extending from altitude 6,000 to 8,000 feet) they were inserting fingers composed of plant representatives from the Plains zone (4,000 to 6,000 feet).

The river bottoms said it was spring by showing color in twigs, the same colors that had marked the twigs all winter, but deeper, brighter, more alive. The osier dogwood was redder, the willows were yellower, or more russet, according to their kind. The narrow-leaved cottonwood was whiter, and the thimbleberry more orange.

North-Facing Slope   Bottomland   South-Facing Slope

On aspens and cottonwoods the catkins bulged under the scales of the winter buds, showing gray on the aspens and brick-red on the cottonwoods.

The prevailing bareness of those colorful twigs told something about the length of summer down there in the Plains zone. Evidently spring comes early enough so that there is plenty of time for growing a new set of leaves and getting full use out of them before frost calls a halt.

Perhaps there was a hint of spring in the footprints we saw at one stop in the foothills, big cat footprints looped around a mountain mahogany bush. Their size, their reach, the way each paw, and evidently the tail too, dragged the snow, made us believe (or perhaps we wanted to believe) that a mountain lion had passed there rather than a lynx or a bobcat. It was easy to visualize his low-slung prowl against moonlit snow, as he hunted such small creatures as might venture out in the milder nights of March.

Back in the car again, we started to climb steadily. At about 8,000 feet we were leaving the Foothills zone behind and entering the Montane zone.

MONTANE ZONE

Douglas fir

Colorado spruce

ponderosa pine

North-Facing Slope   River Bottom   South-Facing Slope

There was no abrupt change in vegetation. Open groves of ponderosa pine were no longer as extensive as they had been in the foothills, but they were still abundant, especially on south-facing slopes. The snow lay in patches there.

Then the north-facing slopes began to present solid black-green stands of Douglas fir rising from deep, unbroken snow.

The river bottoms no longer offered a hint of spring, except possibly in those holes in the ice where black water tumbled past. The bare-twigged trees of the river bottoms were replaced by Colorado spruce.

As we continued to climb through the Montane zone, the ponderosa pine was left behind. Its place was filled by the Douglas fir that had first appeared only on north-facing slopes or in sheltered ravines. The forest, without ponderosa pine, looked different—more compact, with more conical trees.

As we climbed we began to see trees that were narrow spires, growing close together. Those were Engelmann spruces. The first ones we saw were in sheltered ravines and on north-facing slopes.

At 10,000 feet we left the Montane zone and entered the Subalpine zone. The Engelmann spruces were no longer confined to sheltered places. They filled the mountainsides. Douglas firs persisted for a time, but their ranks dwindled fast, and Engelmann spruce and its companion, the alpine fir, took their place.

Places where the spruce-fir forest had been burned were filled with groves of aspen, or with the close-packed match-sticks of lodge pole pine. Incidentally, those lodge-pole pine stands were marking not only the places where forests had been burned, but also places where forests would probably be burned again, soon. Their dead and leaning wood offered ready tinder to any passing spark. We could see the many tightly-closed cones that open at the touch of fire, and thus reseed a burned area. The same fire that consumes a forest may thus be a factor in reseeding it(3).

Occasionally, on some wind-battered knob, we saw a limber pine, bent and beaten, but uncrowded (hazards and blessings of a non-conformist?).

The car skidded, and we had to stop climbing to put on chains. It seemed as if we had turned the calendar back to winter; or as if we had been traveling north at a great rate. By climbing the last 2,000 feet we had seen many of the same changes we might have seen by traveling north through Canada up to the Hudson Bay area at latitude 60 to 66 degrees.

Then we saw timber line, up above us.

A snow plume waved from the mountain ahead, and snow cornices stood out all along the ledge. That was where we first saw skiers come winging down, and where we decided to put on, not skis, but snowshoes. How glad we were that we had brought those snowshoes. The snow was much too deep for walking on without them.

The dark forest of Engelmann spruce was inviting, and we wove our way around the trees' neat narrow spires.

Two features of this forest surprised me. In the Engelmann spruce forests that we had been seeing from the road, on our way up the mountain, the trees had seemed to stand closer together. They had seemed taller, too. The difference was made clear when we talked to the man who was operating the chair-lift. He told us that in the

SUB-ALPINE ZONE

limber pine

Engelmann spruce

Alpine fir and Engelmann spruce

area where we had been walking the official measurement of the snow depth was twenty feet.

We had been walking almost up among the tree tops. After hearing that, we went back and walked again among those trees, just to savor the feeling of twenty feet of snow underfoot.

No wonder that the alpine fir and Engelmann spruce from those close-ranked forests of the Subalpine zone, with their superabundance of water, refuse to grow in our landscape plantings and forestry projects back home in the dry midwest; while limber pine, which, in the Subalpine zone, usually inhabits some wind-swept knob, will succeed for us; and members of the drier, lower altitude forests—ponderosa pine, Douglas fir, junipers—thrive for us.

Several chickadees and a golden-crowned kinglet moved among those treetops where we walked. Were they, at this altitude, a sign of spring, or simply an evidence of the shelter that is offered by such close-packed spires?

If they were a sign of spring, they were doubtless the last sign we would see on that mountaintop, we decided, as we took off our snowshoes and walked over to the ski tow.

That was where we were mistaken.

But it certainly looked as if winter was eternal there, as we sat and soared, up over the gradually shortening spears of Engelmann spruce, up past timber line, up over unbroken fields of snow, to the continental divide.

We got off at the top and walked, with plenty of panting pauses.

We spoke of how we had left spring behind, and of the pasque flower buds that might possibly be huddled under the snow beneath our feet, buds that would probably bloom in July, long after those that we had seen in the foothills had turned into the tousled heads that win them the name "prairie smoke."

As we looked toward mountain ranges hunching to the horizon, with black forests on their shoulders and hips and knees, and their feet somewhere down there in the white mist, we realized that some of those shawled huddles were named the "Never Summer Range."

Was summer never coming there above Berthoud Pass? we wondered.

The answer came speedily, but we did not recognize it at once. It came as I walked, looking far off to the Never Summer Range.

One of my feet sank deep into the snow with a suddenness that toppled me over. I pulled it out, and went on, and sank through again. This time it was not so easy to pull out. I looked down into a surprisingly big cavity, and found that I had one foot tangled in greenness, vivid, alive greenness.

150

Just then my companion went down sideways. As she struggled to get up, she called out, "I'm in a treetop, it seems."

We were not above timber line at all. But we had reached the height at which no tree, or no part of a tree, can endure the winter, except by hiding. We had broken through, down into the hiding place.

As we peered down into these treetops we noticed that they did not terminate in an upright leader shoot, but bore, instead, a tuft of shoots at the tip. Some of the trees had one shoot that did actually extend a few inches above the snow, but that shoot was inevitably dead and dry. The sun and wind and cold had finished it off long before this last week of March.

Suddenly the reason for these strangely shaped trees, the "elfin timber" of timber line, became apparent. Here is the story as it might be told by one of these snow-covered trees:

1. A seed falls and takes root.
   A young shoot starts upward.
   There is plenty of water and sunshine in summer, but summer is only two months long.
2. Winter covers the young spruce deeply with snow.
3. Each summer the little tree grows, both upward and outward.
4. Each winter the snow covers it, completely, but less and and less deeply.
5. One winter the snow barely covers the little tree.
6. In the following summer the tree's leader grows upward as usual.
7. Next winter the snow does not cover the new growth of the leader. The wind dries it; the winter sun reflected from the gleaming snow surface helps to dry it; the cold freezes it. Ice blizzards and hail help to kill it.
8. The following summer another side shoot rises to take the place of the brown, dead leader. It grows, during the summer, just about as high as the first leader had grown.

9. Next winter sun and cold and wind and ice and blizzards and hail kill the new leader.

10. Summer after summer the tree continues its outward growth from the tips of its branches. On the windward side, these branches are dwarfed, or shorn. On the leeward side they elongate steadily. Summer after summer the trunk lays on a new layer of growth.

11. Winter after winter the new leader that rises above snow level is killed. Winter after winter the deep snow lies on the elongated side branches and flattens them.

12. This little tree may grow to be hundreds of years old. Its trunk may be stout with many annual rings. It will not grow any taller.

The story of this tree is repeated again and again just below timber line.

Then we tried to find where timber line really was. We looked for an area that was not punctuated by dead brown spruce or fir tips, an area that would not let us sink through.

There were patches like that, up there, patches where the snow was thin—windy patches. Evidently the full sweep of the wind would not let snow accumulate. Here was no hiding place for firs. They could never have grown more than three or four inches high.

I knelt and pushed away the snow to see if I might uncover the woolly button of an alpine forget-me-not. I brushed against a twig. A woody twig! A line of them! I picked one and looked at it.

Well, a willow twig is a willow twig the wide world over. Its winter buds, with their single foolscap scale, are unmistakable. Those winter buds on that low-growing twig held undeniable promise of spring. This twig was only two inches long. But it sprang, I knew, from a branch that was lying down, in the frozen soil. The trunks of this willow tree were lying down too. Here was the ultimate in tree reduction—a willow that was lying down, the creeping willow, *Salix petrophila*.

We strode across those willows, recalling the regions where we

ELFIN TIMBER tells this story over and over

1 A young Engelmann spruce grows in the brief summer of timberline
.2 Snow covers it deeply through the long winter

3 Each summer the tree gains a little height, a little girth
4 Each winter the snow covers it less and less deeply

5 One winter the snow barely covers the small spruce
6 In the following summer, the tree's leader grows as usual

7 Next winter the snow does not cover the leader, wind and sun dry it, blizzards, hail, and cold help to kill it

8 Next summer a side shoot rises in place of the dead leader

9 Next winter, cold and sun and wind and blizzards and hail kill the new leader

10 Summer after summer the branches grow longer, the trunk grows thicker, the windward side is shorn, and a new leader is lifted up

11 Winter after winter the leader is killed, and the weight of snow flattens the branches

12 The tree may grow to be hundreds of years old, but it will never be taller than the depth of the snow

Such trees often grow close together, forming a continuous mat

could stride across that same willow, or other similarly recumbent ones, in widely separated parts of the earth: Mt. Katahdin, in Maine; Greenland; the barrens about Hudson Bay; Siberia; the Torngat Mountains in Labrador; Gaspé Peninsula, and arctic northwestern America.

Then we headed down the mountains, down towards tree-sized willows—and spring.

In August we came back up the mountainside. We wanted to see the whole of the little trees in whose tops we had been standing in March.

On this trip to Berthoud Pass we could see more than trees and snow. We could see what grew under the trees; and, especially, we could see what replacements for itself each forest was providing.

Down under the ponderosa pines of the foothills there was much grass, most of it brown and dry. Young pines were few, and the ones that were present represented a few distinct ages, not all ages. Probably each group of a uniform size had developed from seedlings that had germinated in a year that was the first in a series of years without fires—enough years for the young trees to develop the ponderosa pine's characteristic thick fire-resistant bark(8). Many of the old pines wore fire scars.

We found some very young seedlings. As we listened to the grass crunching under our feet, we wondered whether those seedlings were not destined to be wiped out soon by fire. On the other hand, the heat of that August sun seemed enough to burn them up without assistance. But we had read(7) that these seedlings had other special equipment for tolerating that dry heat. A ponderosa pine seedling puts down a deep root with outstanding speed. There is no accumulation of duff for it to penetrate, and the porous, well-aerated surface of the foothills favors deep penetration. The fingers of ponderosa forest that extend farthest toward the Plains zone inhabit only the most porous soils(9).

Farther up the mountain we walked for a while in the dense shade of the Douglas fir forests. No dry grass crumbled under our feet. The duff of fallen needles and twigs was much deeper than it had

154

been under the pines; but evidently it was not too deep for Douglas fir seedlings to penetrate. We found enough young trees to see that this forest was replacing itself.

Our next stop was up among the Engelmann spruces. There the duff lay so thick that we wondered, as we poked down through it, how a seedling had time enough, in the abbreviated growing season of this altitude, to penetrate to soil moist enough to carry it through the summer. We did find spruce seedlings, some that had died, and some that had survived. Some of the surviving ones were growing in rotting logs. This had probably favored a more rapid root penetration.

Alpine fir seedlings we did not succeed in finding in that forest(7). We did locate some small trees, but they were not seedlings apparently. They seemed to be growing where branches had been layered firmly into the ground by the weight of snow.

Seedlings of Engelmann spruce and alpine fir, so difficult to find in the forest solidly composed of their own kind, were easy to find in some other types of forest—three other types.

The first place where we found them was in a sunlit aspen grove. Those aspens wore a memory of winter, in the black scars that marked the places where their bark had been nibbled by elk and mule deer when snow covered their usual browse; and in strange stumps that remained from trees the beavers had gnawed off for winter food. One aspen grove held a record of the past, in the form of charred trees, remains of the forest fire that had given the aspens the place in the sun that they require. Another aspen site held a record of more than one fire. The young aspens were root sprouts from the base of an older stand of aspens that had burned. But whatever an aspen stand might have to say about the past it usually predicted a spruce-fir future. In the flower-filled, grassy forest floor, the blue green of Engelmann spruce or alpine fir was conspicuous. (At lower altitudes Douglas fir took their place.)

The second place where we found seedlings of Engelmann spruce and alpine fir was under lodgepole pines, standing so packed on dry slopes (drier than the slopes covered by aspens) that a dead tree

DIAGRAM OF VEGETATION ZONES

on an east slope, with sheltered ravine and some burned areas

- burned areas
- Engelmann spruce or alpine fir
- young Engelmann spruce or alpine fir
- trembling aspen
- lodgepole pine
- Douglas fir
- young Douglas fir
- Colorado spruce
- ponderosa pine
- young ponderosa pine
- Rocky Mountain juniper
- narrow-leaved cottonwood
- box-elder
- willow

sub-alpine zone

montane zone

foothills zone

plains zone

Each tree shown is magnified and represents many of its kind could not fall down. The dry tinder of dead lower branches worn by each tree (unless it stood at the edge of a clearing) cracked as we poked our way into the deep shade. These branches indicated that this was not a shade-tolerant tree but, like the aspen, a pioneer that had seized a fire-made place in the sun. Like the aspen, too, it would not be able to replace itself in its own shade. But the seedlings of the shade-tolerant Engelmann spruce and alpine fir were present, predicting a future spruce-fir forest, if fire stayed away from the tinder-box that was their nursery.

The third place where we found young seedlings of spruce was not in the shade of nurse trees. It was up near timber line where a forest had burned many years ago. There the altitude was too great for aspen and lodgepole pine. But out in the sun and wind, seedling spruces were appearing here and there among the old whitened skeletons of the forest. Slowly, so slowly, the Engelmann spruce was replacing itself, without benefit of pioneers.

Willow
seven years of growth

At the upper limits of the spruce-fir forest we took to the ski lift again.

This trip we rode behind a flamingoed sport shirt, and a pair of waving open-toed shoes, instead of the Norwegian sweaters and skis that we had ridden behind in March. We were anxious to see the pygmy-sized willows that we had found up there under the snow, and the little spruce trees in whose tops we had stood.

Not far from the place where we alighted from the ski lift we found, in an open meadow, a ground cover of glistening willow leaves, with seed heads formed among them. On a small twig separated from the mass, the record of the last seven years of growth was easily read.

Then we walked over to the compact mats of "elfin timber." The tree-tops that we had broken into from above, in March, were about four or five feet from the ground. We inspected the top of one tree. Its story was plainly written. There was the cluster of dead twigs, drooping from the point at which they had once been uplifted, too high. There was the new green upright twig, also uplifted too high, and doomed to death next winter. There beside the green upright one was the brown twig that took the wind above the snow level last winter.

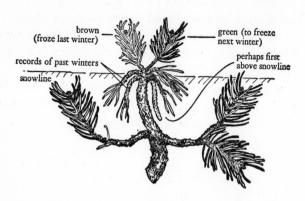

As we crumbled those dry needles between our fingers we realized that, for all the changes we had witnessed from lower timber line to upper timber line, changes in quality of greenness, in root length, in thickness of needles, in tree shapes, in surface cover, in porosity of soil, in temperature, in depth of snow—there was one outstanding feature that was the same at the beginning and at the end of the trip. At the lower tree-line plants were facing a lack of water, an actual lack—a physical drought. At upper tree-line the high wind(9) that takes water from leaves when the intake down below is stopped or slowed by cold, was causing a physiological drought.

In traveling from tree-line to tree-line, we had traveled from drought to drought.

REFERENCES

1. "Plant Zones in the Rocky Mountains of Colorado" by Frances Ramaley. *Science* **26** (1907), 642-643.
2. *New Manual of Botany of the Central Rocky Mountains (Vascular Plants)* by John Merle Coulter. Revised by Aven Nelson. American Book Company, New York, 1909.
3. *The Life History of Lodgepole Burn Forests* by Frederic Edward Clements (U.S. Department of Agriculture, Forest Service Bulletin 79). Government Printing Office, Washington, D.C., 1910.
4. *Plants of Rocky Mountain National Park* by Ruth Ashton. U.S. Govt. Printing Office, Washington, D.C., 1933.
5. "Timberlines in the Northern Rocky Mountains" by R. F. Griggs. *Ecology* **19** (1938), 548-564.
6. *Mountains and Moorlands* by W. H. Pearsall. William Collins and Sons, London.
7. "Vegetational Zonation in the Rocky Mountains" by R. F. Daubenmire. *The Botanical Review* **9** (June, 1943), 325-393.
8. "Fire Damage in the Ponderosa Pine Type in Idaho" by C. A. Connaughton, *Journal of Forestry* **34** (1936), 46-51.
9. *Forest Types in the Central Rocky Mountains at Affected by Temperature and Soil* by C. G. Bates (U.S. Department of Agriculture Bulletin 1263). Government Printing Office, Washington, D.C., 1924.
10. "Phytogeographical Notes on the Rocky Mountain Region IV. Forests of the Subalpine and Montane Zones," by P. A. Rydberg. *Torrey Botanical Club Bulletin* **42** (1915), 11-25.

10.

TUNDRA HAILSTORM
or
Above Timber Line in the Rockies

THE hail was the last straw.

First of all the radiator had boiled, but none of us had minded that. At the sight of the rusty geyser spraying the dusty hood, against the blue backdrop of Observation Point, we had piled out with one accord, crossed the road, and started to climb.

We hadn't climbed far beyond the dwarf trees of timber line, in the relentless sun, before the wind attacked with such sudden fury that we stood close together for a few minutes, arms locked and heads bowed. Then we found a sheltering tor, where our grandchild and her mother could collect shining bits of quartz, and feldspar, and schist, while they stayed behind, near the cooling car to wait for us. The child's finger pointed out a fairy primrose that had found the same shelter and was growing, an inch high, in a tiny Gothic niche.

Soon the wind let us go on, but the sun had become overcast, and the cold needled each of us into making some adjustment, such as buttoning up a sweater, or putting on mittens, or letting down ear flaps, or pulling up socks, or rolling down jeans.

We started out again.

And then the hail found us. We added raincoats, and bowed our heads and hugged ourselves to reduce our vulnerable surfaces.

A flash of lightning reminded us that we had been warned "not to make lightning rods of ourselves" on a barren height.

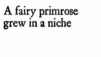

A fairy primrose
grew in a niche

At the thought, I stooped lower and looked down to discover that I was huddled over a group of plants that seemed to be huddling too. Gray-green cushions of plants, they were, there at my knees among the gray-green folds of my raincoat.

Hail-stones lay among the cushion plants

Suddenly we seemed to understand each other, those gray-green cushions and I, because we were meeting the weather in such similar ways. Three of the five cushions at my knees were wearing sweaters, woolly, buttoned up at the neck, with ear muffs pulled down, and socks pulled up. Two of them looked as if they were wearing glistening raincoat material on their tiny leaves. They were crouched much lower than I, but they had to face the full round of the year, and I could leave when conditions grew worse.

My hand lens showed that one of them wore a coat of wax, comparable to the protective coat of face cream that we had used

161

against the elements, and that one of them had sticky globules exuding from its hairlike glands.

They had no shoulders to hunch, or necks to pull in, or heads to bow, but two of them had the edges of their leaves rolled under.

Some leaves of the tundra (much enlarged):

hairy   slick   glandular   edges inrolled

Huddled there, listening to the hailstones spitting, bouncing, rattling, off my raincoat, and watching them bouncing off the gray-green cushion plants, I thought how hard, how stony, how spitting, was the vocabulary of a mountaintop.

"Rock, cirque, tor, peak, scree, tarn, tundra, alp, scarp, crevasse, bluff, cliff, crag." I said them aloud to hear how hard they sounded; and when I explained, the others considered for a minute, and then added other pebbly words of the mountaintop.

Stony words—

"Granite, quartz, gneiss, schist, mica."
"Goat, elk, and coney."
"Finch, hawk, pipit."

What a lot of blunt hard rubble those words are that have attached themselves to the tundra, where almost everything seems to be shaped like a stone, or colored like a stone, or to have a name like a stone, or to be a stone. No words here for lullabies.

162

The sun came out, and immediately we were down on our knees, looking at all the flowers that glistened white, yellow, pink, blue, among the melting moth balls of hail.

I was examining a plant about the size and shape of a winter coat button, that was almost covered with flowers, twenty-one of them, as icy white as the hailstones, when suddenly a bee appeared above those white faces—a bee whose body covered five flowers at a time.

Watching the bee in the sun, I realized that the rigors of climate, tempered for me by raincoat, sweater, face cream, and huddling, were only a fraction of the plants' problems on the mountaintop.

A bee on a
tundra cushion

They have the problem of keeping their pollen dry; the problem of a scarcity of pollinators; the problem of ice blizzards and winter winds that give little rest to snow; the problem of holding on to rock in the face of sliding snow and gouging rains; the problem of holding on to bits of soil and decayed leaves, and moisture, against ice and torrents, parching sun, and drying winds; and the problem of ten months of winter followed by summer days that run the gamut, every twelve hours, of all the season's changes.

We started examining plant after plant to see what features they had in common, what features seemed to make survival possible.

The leaves, certainly, had several characteristics in common.

They were small. Their size brought the memory of other small leaves: those of fir and spruce in the north; of aromatic sumac in the Bad Lands of South Dakota; of heather on windswept dunes in Denmark; of cranberries in a cold and acid bog; of hudsonia in

163

sand dunes; of creeping snowberry on the edge of a northern bog; of cactus in the desert. It was easy to understand that leaves of the mountaintop should be small.

Some of the leaves were smooth with a waxy finish that reminded my fingertips of the feel of wintergreen and balsam fir of the north; of the waxy coat of the century plant; and of the resinous covering of the creosote bush of the desert.

Many of the leaves were woolly, with dense overlapping hairs. Feeling them, I recalled lead plant in the Illinois prairie; mullein in sun-beaten pastures; Russian olive in the windbreaks of Nebraska; sagebrush on the Great Plains; the underside of the leaves of Labrador tea; the hairy lip fern of dry, rocky ledges; and the edelweiss of the Alps.

Many, many of the leaves were fat, thick, or succulent. They reminded me of the many fat-leaved plants that face the wind on the bare bluffs of the Pacific coast south of Monterey; and the crassula that went on growing, even blooming, when we were trying to dry it in a plant press at the university; and the balloon-shaped leaves on a specimen from a salt marsh; and the fatness of the bryophyllum leaf that tourists send home from Florida so that their friends may pin it on a curtain and watch it develop new plants; and the Russian thistle of Minnesota roadsides; and the purslane of every hoof-beaten farmyard; and the little succulents that grow in the backs of china elephants in the desert air of Chicago apartments, needing only to be dusted off with the rest of the furniture. It was not surprising to meet fleshy leaves with water storage facing the summer sun of the mountaintop.

Many had stems or leaves or leaf margins set with glands that were tipped with a sticky knob. Through the hand lens those sticky knobs, reflecting the sharp sun, reminded me of the abundant glands on a catchfly on sun-beaten sand, and the amber globules on bayberry leaves along the Maine coast, and the glands on rose geranium and peppermint and sweetbrier rose.

Many of the leaves were inrolled at the margin, toward the underside. This inrolled, or revolute, leaf margin marks northern firs, bog rosemary, swamp laurel of high cold ponds, Labrador tea of the arctic tundra, sweetfern of stony New England pastures. Some grasses roll up in a drought, and some mosses fold up and roll up into dead-looking brown hairs. When one remembers that the microscopic openings into the moist inner parts of the leaves are situated on those protected under surfaces, it is not hard to understand that there should be some revolute margins on the mountaintop.

There was one feature of the leaves that might have been surprising if we had read about it in a book instead of seeing it on these plants. They had "entire," or evenly continuous, margins, almost all of them—margins without saw teeth or lobes. In view of the consistently deeply divided leaves on the plants of roadsides, prairies, and pastures, these entire leaves might have seemed out of place, except for the obvious fact that they were already so drastically reduced in size that any further reduction seemed almost impossible.

Next we inspected the flowers.

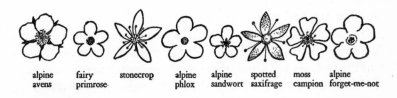

| alpine
avens | fairy
primrose | stonecrop | alpine
phlox | alpine
sandwort | spotted
saxifrage | moss
campion | alpine
forget-me-not |

Their pattern had a conspicuous sameness. They were flat-faced, circular, five-parted, small (though their smallness was not in proportion to the smallness of their leaves); they were held side by side, almost overlapping, but not quite; and they were short-stemmed or stemless. In color they were white or yellow or pale pink, for the most part. Many had hairs in their throats.

As the hailstones melted, it was understandable that these flowers could profit by hairs or scales obstructing their throats, helping to keep the pollen dry and the nectar undiluted by the sudden rain, hail, or snow of the brief mountaintop summer.

The massed formation of those minute flowers was akin to the compact community of a sunflower head, where each floret cooperates with many others in achieving a massed showiness that will attract an insect. The flowers of a mountaintop need to be small to endure the weight of the weather, and, being small, they need to pool their showiness.

Since flower stems are a hazard in the gales, the round disk pattern is best for the flower. Side-entranced, or irregular, flowers fit best on a spike. What few flower spikes were found on the tundra were short, short ones, and compact.

We looked then at the plant form—the whole plant.

Cushions, cushions, cushions.

When we dug up one cushion to inspect it, we found that it consisted not only of matted gray-green leaves and short stems, but also of all the precious old organic material of its own manufacture that it had hoarded to itself. Down below, enmeshed in the matted growth, were old brown leaves, old seed capsules emptied of their contents, and old dead stalks, with a few crumbs of soil.

Here was no spendthrift economy.

Because we had so recently taken precautions to make secure all our loose paraphernalia, such as bandannas and caps, when the wind struck, we could visualize what it meant for a plant to hold on to the treasure of humus, there on the mountaintop. Those compact little cushions clutching their old parts reminded me of pioneers who made rugs of their rags, of frogs that eat their discarded skins, of gardeners who accumulate compost piles, and of those Chinese peasants who hoard the family excrement to enrich the garden where the family food is grown.

This cushion plant with its hoarded dry parts makes an efficient sponge for soaking up water. It is efficient, too, in covering the ground beneath it so closely that water can hardly evaporate. This use of the hemispherical form, which exposes as little surface as possible to the thirsty sun and wind, is not unlike other uses of the sphere and halfsphere, in places where it is essential to have as much volume as possible with a minimum of surface—spheroidal gas tanks, and certain echinoderms, and cushion cactus, for example.

We dug up other cushions to see what sort of roots they had. Thick, distorted, ancient-looking taproots they were. A botanist in Switzerland, who counted the annual rings of growth on such heavy old roots of alpine forget-me-not, told of finding plants that were more than thirty years old(1). Others have told of counting more than a hundred rings. And the thickness of the rings has sometimes been found to measure one thirty-four-thousandth of a millimeter.

Alpine forget-me-not

old, thick taproot

These plants inherit dwarfness; they are not simply dwarfed forms of plants from lower altitudes. Experiments in transplanting them have proved this fact(10).

But it was not only the possession of certain features in common that marked these tundra plants. It was also the absence of certain other features.

There were, of course, no trees, unless the creeping willow was to be called a tree because of the stature of its relatives. No living thing could stand tall and live through the buffeting and gouging of winter. We had left the trees behind down where they were ancient stunted forms without hope of growing higher than the depth of winter snows.

A thought-provoking absence was that of the dependents. There were apparently no saprophytes, no parasites, no epiphytes, no climbers even. That absent company was composed of plants that flourish where the living is soft, food abundant, and growth flaccid. There were hangers-on at the Roman banquets; and Lazarus lay under the rich man's table, but Saint John the Baptist ate his locusts and wild honey alone.

There was an absence of bulbs and of fleshy rhizomes—absence, in short, of all sorts of vulnerable softness.

Annuals were almost entirely absent. It would be too much to expect of any plant that it should germinate, grow, flower, and mature seeds in that brief summer with so much of winter mixed in it. The wind had abated and the sun had grown hot. We took off coats and sweaters and sat down to rest, and to hunt up some of these strangers in our flower books.

Their common names were of some interest. They showed that hail and wind and cold had not shriveled the imagination of those who had given the everyday names to these flowers. There were Sky Pilot, Snowlover, Old Man of the Mountain, Fairy Primrose, Gem Carpet, Skyland Willow, Mountain Dryad.

The genus names, too, held some interest, for they revealed relationships. It was not surprising to find Silene and Lychnis, Sedum, Primula, and Artemisia, nor to find Betula and Potentilla, Aster, and Solidago, because a botanist expects to find those genera inhabiting the world's open, sun-beaten places. Nor was it surprising to find Saxifraga, Campanula, and Aquilegia, because a botanist is used to seeing those genera sitting on rock. The very name Saxifraga means "rock breaker."

But it was the species names that were most revealing, because, while genus names carry a picture of the floral structure, a species name often has something to tell of the way in which a particular member of the genus has had its stature, its texture, its character shaped by adversity, opportunity, and time.

Whenever a list of flowers contains a preponderance of the following species names, one may assume that that company has faced sun and wind, cold and heat, hail and gouging rains, drought and blizzards.

168

Some of the species names have alp and mountain in them:

>*alpestris*
>*montana*
>*saximontana* (rock mountain)
>*austromontana* (southern mountains)
>*monticola* (a small mountain)
>*scopulorum* (of the rocks)
>*oreophilum* (mountain-loving)

Some have the north, and cold, and snow, in them:

>*boreale*
>*hyperboreale*
>*groenlandica*
>*frigida*
>*nivea* (snow)

Some tell of protection:

>*glaucophylla* (blue-gray-green of leaf; a reminder of our raincoats)
>*hirsutissima* (extremely hairy; a reminder of our sweaters)
>*glandulosa* (covered with the sticky knobs of glands; a reminder of our face cream)

Some tell of pulling in their necks:

>*nanum* (dwarf)
>*pygmaea*
>*condensata*
>*repens* (creeping)
>*reptans* (crawling)
>*procumbens*
>*prostrata*
>*humilis* (low or slight)
>*acaulis* (stemless)
>*caespitosa* (tufted)

Some of them have names that are filled with human interest because they are the names of the botanists and naturalists and explorers who first found these alpine plants. As we read their names we saw an adventuresome band, wearing ear muffs and carrying green vasculums and plant presses, and peering through microscopes with eyes accustomed to looking at far-off big things such as mountain passes and portages and Indian fires, as well as nearby small things, such as stamens and pistils. It was a goodly company:

Parryi (for Charles Christopher Parry, 19th century botanist who explored remote places, and discovered hundreds of new species, of which fifty bear his name)

Rydbergii (for Per Axel Rydberg, western botanical explorer who, in 1900, compiled a flora of Montana and Yellowstone Park)

Coulteri (for John Merle Coulter, world-renowned botanist of the University of Chicago, who compiled a Rocky Mountain flora)

Douglasi (for David Douglas, Scottish botanist who in the early 1800's collected plants from America's Northwest for the Horticultural Society of London)

Engelmannii (for George Engelmann, 19th century botanical explorer and writer)

Some of them have species names that are of geographical interest, and so started us off on the old line of speculation about plants called "disjuncts." (In this book we have met disjuncts in several chapters: Bog, Dunes, Canyon, Smokies.) Two such species names were:

sajanensis (from Saiansk mountains, Siberia)

beeringianum (from the region of the Bering Sea)

Some of the species that are disjuncts, because they grow in the Rockies, and in several faraway places, from which this colony is widely separated, are the moss campion, the mountain dryad, and the alpine forget-me-not.

The mountain dryad, a shrub that is lying down, forming dwarf creeping mats, grows also in the White Mountains, in Greenland, in Alaska, and in alpine and arctic Europe and Asia. It is perhaps as typical a mountaintop shrub as one could find.

The moss campion grows also in Greenland, in the Alps, in

Asia, in New Hampshire, and in alpine to arctic situations from New Mexico to Alaska. The alpine forget-me-not grows also in the Alps.

These widely separated patches of a species have sometimes been considered to be the result of bird distribution of seeds. But we know now that seeds do not travel great distances in the digestive systems of birds(4, 12).

Mountain dryad, Dryas octopetala—a shrub that is lying down

also found in:
White Mountains,
Alaska,
Greenland,
arctic and
alpine Europe,
and Asia

— inrolled edges
— wax deposit

glandular
below flower

Such plants, that seem to hop from mountaintop to mountaintop and from arctic tundra to the mountaintops, leaping plains, and lakes, and deserts, and forests, and oceans, are usually recording cold rather than birds.

During the glacial periods, northern vegetation was pushed southward. The glacial cold, added to the cold of altitude, must have clothed some mountains with tundra that extended much further down the mountainside than it now does. Thus, that tundra was often continuous from mountaintop to mountaintop across intervening valleys.

South   North

tundra

When the ice and cold retreated gradually to the north, the evergreen trees advanced up the mountainsides, crowding the

171

tundra plants into the less favorable places, the places where living conditions were still too rugged for evergreens.

Islands of tundra were left behind on the mountaintops.

Deciduous forests began to push up from the south, invading the foothills and the mountain valleys. Meanwhile erosion was helping to cut the islands of tundra apart.

In the arctic region, as the ice sheet retreated, there was tundra encircling the globe, with peninsulas of tundra running south along the nearest mountains. Then oceans cut the arctic tundra apart.

Gradually, then, isolated patches of plants were left, far from their kind, until today, a mountaineer may meet a flower which he has learned to know in the Rockies, growing also in the Alps, in Scandinavia, in the Pyrenees, in the Himalayas, in the Altai Mountains, as well as in Greenland, in Spitzbergen, and in arctic Russia (2, 7).

During the long years of separation, some of these isolated communities have produced members that show differences from their ancestral kind, differences that have survived because they made them better fitted to endure the hardships of their mountaintop.

These remote members of some mountaintop species may meet each other some day, if cold again comes creeping down from the north. Then, if Edgar Anderson(3) is right about the areas in which the greatest number of variations occur in plants, a great number of variations should crop up.

The hail started again. We left the gray cushions to face the pelting and the freezing night temperature that threatened, and we retreated down the mountain to conditions that encourage parasites and climbers and vulnerable softness.

REFERENCES

1. *Mountains in Flower* by Volkmar Vareschi and Ernst Krause. Macmillan, New York, 1940.
2. "The Vegetation of Alpine Region of the Rocky Mountains in Colorado" by Theodore Holm. Memoir *National Academy of Science* **19,** Number 3, (1923), 5-45.
3. *Plants, Man and Life,* by Edgar Anderson. Little, Brown, Boston, 1952.
4. *Historical Plant Geography,* by E. V. Wulff (of U.S.S.R. Institute of Plant Industry, Leningrad). Chronica Botanica Company, Waltham, Massachusetts, 1943.
5. *Colorado Plant Life* by Francis Ramaley. University of Colorado, Boulder, 1927.
6. *New Manual of Botany of the Central Rocky Mountains (Vascular Plants)* by John Merle Coulter. Revised by Aven Nelson. American Book Company, New York, 1909.
7. *Natural Regions of the U.S.S.R.,* by L. S. Berg. Chapter X, Mountains of the Caucasus. Macmillan, New York, 1950.
8. *The Geography of the Flowering Plants,* by Ronald Good. Chapters 8-11, Distribution of Species. Longmans, Green and Co., London & New York, 1947.
9. "Alpine Vegetation in the Vicinity of Long's Peak, Colorado," by W. S. Cooper. *Botanical Gazette* **45** (1908), 319-337.
10. "The Causes of Dwarfing in Alpine Plants" by F. E. Clements. *Science* **25** (1908), 287.
11. "The Alpine Zone, in Vegetational Zonation in the Rocky Mountains," by R. F. Daubenmire. *The Botanical Review* **9** (June, 1943).
12. "Adventures in Mountain Botany" by Hugh M. Raup in *The Friendly Mountains: Green, White and Adirondacks,* edited by Roderick Peattie. Vanguard, New York, 1942.
13. "Flowers in the Arctic" by Rutherford Platt. *Scientific American* (February, 1956), 89-98.

11.

READIN', 'RITIN',
AND RECESS

or

Tree Rings in a Country Schoolyard

THE first time we passed that corner was during the summer. Someone in the back seat said:

"Look! There! Isn't that a little cupola, or bell tower, or something, in that thicket?"

"Schoolhouse, probably," grunted the driver. "Shall I back up?"

We decided to investigate next time.

It was November when we came that way again. The little bell tower and half-boarded windows squinted out through weedy saplings.

As we pushed through the thicket it became apparent that, within the last few days, the roof had been mended with a few shingles, and several of the saplings that grew out of the very foundation had been sawed off.

"This school must have been closed some years ago," said one of our group, feeling the thickness of the saplings around the front stoop.

174

"Let's see if we can read the clues well enough to tell just when the school closed down," someone suggested, and we all agreed. "We" were one geologist, one teacher, and two botanists.

The geologist turned at once to the stout masonry walls of the school building, and to the cement floor that indicated the former position of a coal shed. There was still coal dust, and a few chunks of coal, left.

The teacher found a board that others had used, and braced it against the side of the building beneath a window and scrambled up and over.

We two botanists turned to the plants.

Presently we pooled our findings.

The geologist, tongue in cheek, narrowed time down cautiously out of the past.

"We can safely assume that the building was constructed well after the Silurian (some 300 million years ago), inasmuch as Niagara limestone, laid down under a Silurian sea, has been used at the corners and for window lintels. We can further narrow it down to post-glacial times on the evidence of the schoolyard's being glacial drift containing bits of Canadian rocks; and also on the evidence of the masonry walls, which are built of glacial boulders, bigger ones within, and small fist-sized ones carefully collected and laid up in rows on the outside finish.

"But a careful inspection of those ingredients of the wall reveals lime mortar, and also the fact that not all those cobblestones are natural ones; a few are man-made, and those green glassy lumps might have been bottles. That narrows us down to the industrial age, even without the help of the two boards over the entrance that bear the inscription:

S. S. Dickinson

A. D. 1855

"Those two artifacts bring us right down to the September morning when the president of the Board of Directors, probably S. S. Dickinson himself, tied his horse to the hitching post beside the mud road, and went around to the other side of the surrey to help the probably high-collared, long-sleeved, pompadoured, young teacher get her several long skirts over the wheel.

"So much for the opening of the school, but when it comes to dating the closing, I find few clues that speak to a geologist. There is the coal that still remains on the floor of the former coal shed, and there is no coal in the crack that has formed in the foundation. That crack, however, seems to have been made by a tree root, so that I should be encroaching on the field of my colleagues if I were to include that among my clues. There is a worn place on the window ledge—a form of differential erosion—that might indicate how long people have been entering through the window. But it is probable that the windows held against the public for several years after the school closed."

Then we added a little differential erosion to the window ledge, as we four scrambled up and over.

Evidently the schoolroom equipment, stove, desks, organ, cupboard, had, as with most schoolhouses hereabouts, been sold at public auction. The blackboard had not been sold because it was no more than a black painted strip across the front wall, above the built-in recitation benches. But, when buyers removed cupboard and desks, they evidently dumped their contents on the floor. No books were there; those, too, must have been sold. But there were scraps and torn fragments; enough for us, who had each been a teacher at some time, to piece together the educational era that had been in sway at the time the school closed.

Palmer-method writing, for one thing, with its rows of fifteen capital A's to the line, pointed back at least twenty-five years, even allowing for a possible educational lag out here in the country.

Phonetic reading (back in style again today), from flash cards with "hop, top" or "fond, pond" on them, was there. We found no sign of the next era that started right in with whole sentences such as "Run with me to the tree."

Among the scraps was a bluejay picture, in outline, colored in with crayons. A soiled, stepped-on card cheerily said, "It is a bright,

176

sunny morning." There were two Perry pictures, "The Return of the Mayflower" and Corot's "Spring"; but no colored pictures, unless the coloring had been done by the pupils, as suggested on the page torn from a Second Grade Reader:

Relicts inside,
pioneers outside

"Riddles"

"I am little.
I am brown.
You are good to me.
You give me bread and water.
I like bones, too.
I find your ball for you.
What am I?
Draw me. Color me. Draw what I find for you.
Color it red."

Two clues here! 1. A dog talking like a human! Anthropomorphism, educators would stamp it today, with a shudder. 2. "Color it red." No chance for a child to express himself, by coloring it chartreuse, or putting square corners on it, or a mustache!

Another clue, mixed with fallen plaster, was the nature of the titles that appeared on scraps of textbooks—titles such as "Africa," "Inventions," "Seeds." In a modern textbook such subjects might,

177

or might not, be touched upon under a larger concept, such as "The World We Live In," or "Finding New Ways To Do Things," or "How Men Get Along." (The same difference between titles would probably crop up today between the answers of teacher and pupil if asked, "What are you having in your class?" The teacher might say, "How Living Things Rest," while the pupil, unprodded, or the teacher, if tired, might blurt out, "Seeds." But we have long ago learned to look for primitive characteristics in unprodded children and tired adults.)

Remnants of "busy work" lay in one corner—a card punctured into a picture of a Sunbonnet Baby, for sewing; a mat woven out of narrow strips of wallpaper. As I automatically started to put right the strip that had skipped a place, I visualized the small hands that had left the mat unfinished, baffled by that strip; the backs of the hands I visualized were stiff with chilblains, as hands had been stiff in the country school where I had taught forty-odd years ago.

There was no trace of "meaningful activity"—no orange crates, no hammers, no balsa wood, no test tubes.

The teacher gave her verdict on the date of the school's closing. Between eighteen and twenty-five years ago, she said.

We wandered out into the entry where the coat hooks still made a neat row, and a stout bell cord still hung. But the cord had been tied to a rafter when the bell was sold. We found the shelf for the water bucket, the ruffled parts of what had evidently been ruffled dotted swiss curtains, and a corner of a school flag.

Then it was the botanists' turn to show how well plants can record the passing of time.

We turned first of all to the three bur oaks. They looked like old settlers, but not old enough to have passed the crest of their muscular vigor.

One of the oaks was a natural "climbing tree." Many a pair of stout, home-knit, ribbed wool stockings held up by garters from a Ferris waist must have suffered from that ridged bark.

Those trees must often have served as "gools" for games; and their acorns must have been handy ammunition for schoolground battles. We walked on ground that was pebbled with them.

But what of the three acorns from which these trees had grown? When and how did they get their start? They must have germinated after Indians and their prairie fires were gone from this area They would not have been big enough or corky-barked enough to resist those fires as mature bur oaks are able to resist them.

But how at that time did they escape being cropped off, with the grass, by wandering cattle? Fences were scarce; osage-orange hedges were small; and barbed wire and lawn-mowers were not yet available.

We turned away from the oak, undecided about its place in the chronology of the schoolground; and gave our attention to the elm that stood in the middle of the side yard. About fifty or sixty years ago someone must have planted it there, and given it adequate protection against damage during games at recess—else it could not have survived.

Two trees on the schoolground might well have been Arbor Day trees. In 1872 Arbor Day was started, in Nebraska, and soon spread to Illinois. One of the trees was a sugar maple; the other was a Scotch pine. Both had been well located to leave the front part of the ground open so that farmers could pull their rigs in off the road there, when they came to Speaking Schools, or Spell-downs, or Box Sociables.

Two other plants had been brought in, a black locust out beside the road on the west, and a little bush near the northwest corner of the building.

There were two gaps in time represented by the trees of the schoolground: one large gap between the age of the bur oaks and the pine-elm-sugar maple-locust-lilac group; one smaller gap between this group and the tangle of saplings. Many young elms made up that tangle, as well as young locusts, several young bur oaks, a few young ash, and a close thicket of young wild black cherry.

Among the young trees, one size predominated, the size of the largest specimens. We concluded that this dominant size indicated the group that started to grow on the schoolground in the first year after the school was closed down and the grass was no longer kept cut. We concluded further that the gap between the ages of mature bur oaks and the thicket trees represented years during which the grass had been kept cut. On the west side of the grounds alone, there were twenty-five trees of dominant size.

We counted some of their bud-scale scars, starting at the tips of the highest twigs and going downward. These scars, left when the protective scales are shed by an opening winter bud, were easy to count for the last eight or ten years, but scars of previous years had become obscure. By estimating that the earlier growth would have been only a little more rapid than the later, we concluded that these trees had started growing about eighteen to twenty-two years ago.

Then we turned to the five trees that had very recently, probably within the last week, been sawed down. Two of these were close against the foundation on the east side, so that they must have been growing directly up past the windows there.

We counted their concentric rings—nineteen.

There were several trees growing up close around the front stoop. All of them were of the dominant size, the same size as the elm that had been cut down on the east side of the building, and two locusts that had been cut down on the west side.

Beside those two locusts a pear tree had also been cut. All three of these showed nineteen rings.

A sprawly apple tree, uncut, was growing up out of the foundation on the east side. A few wormy, distorted apples lay on the ground under it.

At first thought the trees that blocked the entrance seemed to be the most telltale ones. Certainly they would not have been tolerated there when school was in session, and they would have been trampled to death as seedlings.

"Granted that they would not have been there while school was in session," said the teacher, "but how do you know that they came in immediately afterward?"

180

"And how do you know," asked the geologist, "that the grass was not kept cut for a few years after the school closed down? I can show you two country schools not far away that have been closed, but still have their grass cut."

Because of these arguments we turned to the apple tree and the cut pear tree for affirmation of our nineteen-year estimate.

No bird brought those seeds; the fruits are too large. And certainly no human deliberately planted either the pear or the apple, either as seed or sapling, in such a position, six inches from a masonry wall. Farmers have more sense than that. But someone might have thrown away a core, or spit out a seed—possibly spit it out through a temporary gap in the front teeth. Probably it was recess, morning recess, in the fall, and probably, for a little boy who wasn't wanted underfoot in the big boys' games, this east wall was a warm place to lean up against. Probably that boy liked apples better than pears. I remember how, in my country school, the best tidbits were eaten from the lunch box during morning recess. Probably the pear seed for the tree on the west side was spit out during afternoon recess.

This must have happened during the last year that school was in session here, otherwise the tender seedlings would have been mown with the grass, or tramped down during games of tag. True, it had to endure through that last spring session, but country schools closed earlier then, and the big boys with the heaviest feet were not there to play "Andy, Andy, over" and "pom-pom-pullaway" after the planting season started.

As we counted and recounted the nineteen rings of the pear stump, we felt again that we were keeping good company; at least we were hovering on the outermost fringe of the good company that has found interesting records in tree rings.

Venerable in that company was John Evelyn, Esquire, writing, in 1664, his "Sylva, or a Discourse of Forest Trees and the Propagation of Timber in His Majesties Dominions." Printed deep, with wooden type, into hand-made paper, we can read his cautious statement about the rings in trees:

181

"It is commonly and very probably asserted, That a Tree gains a new one every year. In the body of a great Oak in the New Forest, cut transversely even (where many of the Trees are accounted to be some hundreds of years old) three and four hundred have been distinguished. In a Fir-tree, which is said to have just so many rows of boughs about it as it is of year's growth, there has been observed just one less immediately above one row then immediately below: Hence some probable account may be given of the difference between the outer and the inner parts of the Rings, that the outermost being newly produced in the Summer, the exterior superficies is condens'd in the Winter."

Outstanding among that company was the astronomer Douglass(8) of Flagstaff, Arizona, extending his vision in one direction with the telescope, toward sunspots; in the other direction with a microscope, toward tree rings, and discovering the same rhythm in both objectives; and then deepening his understanding in the human direction, by a study of pottery patterns, until he was able to find the needed wood for completing his tree-ring calendar that has presented anthropologists with a new tool for dating(9).

Included in that company was Doctor Henry Cowles(3), offering as testimony in an Arkansas lawsuit the tree-ring record that proved that lakes had not been where early survey maps had placed them.

Towering, and most recent, in the company is Doctor Willard Libby(7), first suggesting that cosmic radiation, bombarding the nitrogen envelope of the earth, might split the nitrogen atom, and that one result of the splitting might be radioactive carbon; and then reasoning that this Carbon 14 would become a part of living plants. It was after his Geiger counter had clicked to measure the deterioration of the Carbon 14 in the spruce trees at Two Creeks, Wisconsin, that had been toppled by the glacier, that our estimate of the last glacial invasion had to be moved up from 25,000 to 11,000 years ago. But while the Geiger counter was testing for dates, it was also being put to a test by tree rings. A section from a famous old sequoia tree was used for this test. From this section a bit of the core

182

was taken, because that was the oldest part. The Geiger counter made three counts. The readings were: 3,045 years, 2,404 years, 2,817 years. The rings on the section told the age of the tree as 2,905 years. The average for the Geiger counter readings was 2,710 years. The tree had been cut in 1874.

Farther out toward the fringe of the tree-record readers was Aldo Leopold of Wisconsin, sawing down an old bur oak, and interpreting the story of each ring in his "A Sand County Almanac" (5).

And there was Enos Mills, of Long's Peak, finding records of earthquakes, avalanches, crowding neighbor trees, Indians, heavy snows, woodpeckers, Spaniards, and telling of them in "The Story of a Thousand-Year Pine"(2).

And there is Jesse Stuart (4), another country schoolteacher, conscious of the importance of recesses, telling the story of a man who was able to keep his land only because of the irrefutable story in tree rings.

In 1953, a great white oak blew down in an eastern forest, and revealed in its rings a fire record that seems to support the idea that stands of oak in regions where the dominant forest trees include beech, and sugar maple, usually have fires in their history. The rings told that this tree had started growing in 1627. They showed fire scars, all healed over by vigorous growth, for the years 1641, 1652, 1662, 1676, 1701, 1711. Settlement in this area was in 1701(12).

The rest of the vegetation on our schoolground, other than the trees, had only a few comments to make on the past.

Many pioneers had come in. There were thistle, burdock, curly dock, giant ragweed, dandelion, wild roses, black raspberries, aster, evening primrose, catnip, wild grape, plantain. Together they recorded transportation by wind, by fur, by bird, by man. The plantain's ancestors may have come over on the *Mayflower*.

Out under the big elm, where an automobile party might have stopped for lunch, there was a four-year-old peach tree.

Around the coal-shed foundation the trees were younger. Nine years was the age we read on bud-scale scars of trees growing in cracks of the foundation, and between the foundation and the road. We decided that saplings had been cut nine years ago by the person who had bought the coal shed at the school auction and moved it away.

The future of the schoolground, if man did not intervene, was written plainly. Bur oaks were starting up through the thicket, even on the west side, far from the big oaks. Squirrels must have carried acorns to that corner. It was well on its way back to the same sort of forest that it must once have held. In the most dense spots where shade was deepening, grass and sun-loving pioneers were going, and their places were being taken by typical forest ground covers such as bedstraw.

But evidently man had plans other than a forest. The new shingles and the cut trees spoke of a new venture.

A big yellow school bus, bringing the local farm children home from the graded school at Algonquin, turned the corner.

"I thought I felt the schoolhouse shudder," said the geologist, who had been inspecting a pebble of granite from the edge of Lake Superior, set in the old wall.

We started for home, but we turned in at the first farm lane. No one questioned that stop. We wanted to check our reckoning.

The farmer was in his barn. He said, "Well, yes, I guess I ought to be able to tell you a little something about the old school, but it's been sold already."

We assured him that we didn't want to buy the school, we only wanted to know when it had been closed.

"Well," he said, "I guess I can tell you that all right. Let's see now. I graduated from eighth grade there, myself. I was fourteen then. Five years later I was back there off and on, going steady with the teacher, sort of. She was just out of high school, too, and a week of Teachers Institute. Next year they had a man teacher. Kept him two years. Then there was a girl teacher again. Stayed two years and then married a farmer over there on the

184

River Road. That was the year I got married myself. There was some other girl teaching there that next year. I don't remember her much. But that was the last year. We were married in June, and when school closed next spring it was all fixed already for the kids from this district to go to school in town. Some people kicked about it. That was——that was eighteen, no, nineteen years ago."

He looked at us inquiringly.

"The reason we're so pleased is that we figured out it must have closed nineteen years ago, from the tree rings."

"Good for you," he said in a tolerant manner.

As we left, he pointed to the tool shed.

"There's a part of your old schoolhouse," he said. "That used to be the coal shed, I bought it at the auction, and moved it over here—nine, ten years ago, or so . . ."

As we drove home that day, we did not suspect that those schoolground trees would offer us still more tree-ring evidence.

We passed that way again a few years later. The bell tower no longer peered from a thicket. The thicket had been cut, and a big streamer across the face of the schoolhouse invited the public to enter the real estate office of a new subdivision. Shining cars were parked under the bur oaks, the elm, the Arbor Day trees. The lilac bush was gone.

A year later we sought out the schoolhouse again, and thought, when we reached the site, that we had taken the wrong road. A modern service station stood where the biggest bur oak had been. An expanse of cement, punctured by new gas pumps and a sign that said "Progress" in foot-high letters, covered the site of the schoolhouse. In back of the filling station lay the bur oaks, the elm, the sugar maple, the Scotch pine, the original black locust. They had been bulldozed out of the ground.

Then we saw the schoolhouse itself. Wrapped in stout cables, it had been moved on to a new high cement foundation to the east of the former school grounds. The bell tower was gone; the wooden shingles covered with roofing paper, and there were new

bur oak
seedlings

bur oak
seedling

First day—1855

bur oak

elm

bur oak

pine

maple

locust

lilac

Last day—1933

peach

cherry

elms

pear

locusts

Eighteen years later

school

bur oaks

maple

elm

pine

Three years later
One hundred years after first day

two-paned windows. Out beyond it and the tumbled trees we could see several new ranch houses.

The upturned roots of the trees answered one of our questions about the bur oaks' beginnings. They held no trace of rich deep prairie earth in their clutches, only the pale clay of oak openings. This corner had probably been cleared to make a school site.

There was one more question—the age of the bur oaks.

We hunted up the owner of the schoolhouse, and found his wife at home. She had been a schoolteacher in the next district, and had come over to the cobblestone schoolhouse for box sociables. She regretted, with tears in her eyes, the passing of the bur oaks, and gave us permission to cut a slice from the largest trunk.

We got the slice, and counted the rings.

The tree was the same age as the school.

Probably the three oak seedlings owed their chance of survival to a thicket that developed on the line between school land and farm land. Perhaps hawthorn trees, keeping cows at bay, made a good oak nursery. A board fence may have helped. By the time the lawn was mowed, the young oaks would have attained enough stature to be respected by the mower.

Life had been easy there on the school ground, the tree rings, broad and evenly-spaced, said, with recesses to eliminate any springtime seedlings that might have developed into competitors for sun and rain, and with long peaceful summer vacations for untrammeled growing.

It seemed not unfitting that the trees that had been born with the cobblestone schoolhouse should die with it. On our way home that day we passed two great heaps of bur oaks that had been bulldozed out so that the land could be flattened for the even spacing of houses in a new subdivision. The time has passed, in that countryside, for country schools and bur oaks.

REFERENCES

1. *Sylva, or a Discourse of Forest Trees and the Propagation of Timber in His Majesties Dominions,* by John Evelyn. Royal Society, London, 1664.

2. *The Story of a Thousand-Year Pine, and Other Tales of Wild Life,* by Enos Abijah Mills. Houghton Mifflin, Boston, 1913.

3. "The Trees That Won a Lawsuit," in *Book of Plants,* by Bertha Parker and Henry C. Cowles. Houghton Mifflin, Boston, 1925.

4. Testimony of Trees, from *Clearing in the Sky,* by Jesse Stuart, Whittlesey House, N. Y., 1951.

5. *A Sand County Almanac and Sketches Here and There,* by Aldo Leopold. Oxford, New York, 1949.

6. *Radiocarbon Dating,* by Frederick Johnson. Society for American Archeology, Salt Lake City, Utah, 1951.

7. *Radiocarbon Dating,* by Willard F. Libby. University of Chicago Press, Chicago, 1952.

8. *Sun Spots in Action,* by Harley True Stetson. Chapter on Tree-Rings. The Ronald Press, New York, 1947.

9. *Tree-Ring Analysis and Dating in the Mississippi Drainage,* by Florence Hawley. The University of Chicago Publications in Anthropology, University of Chicago Press, Chicago, 1941.

10. "The Phytosociology of an Oak Woods in Southeastern Wisconsin" by Grant Cottam, *Ecology* **30,** 271-287.

11. *Dating Prehistoric Ruins by Tree Rings,* by W. S. Stallings, Jr. Revised edition published by The Tree-Ring Society with the co-operation of the Laboratory of Tree-Ring Research, University of Arizona, Tucson, 1949.

12. "Fire in the History of Mettler's Woods" by Murray F. Buell, Helen F. Buell and John A. Small. *Bulletin of Torrey Botanical Club* **81** (1954), 253-255.

12.

LOOKING DOWN ON
IMPROVED PROPERTY

or

An Airplane View of Man and Land

THE two men with brief cases, waiting beside me at Gate 5, were bragging to each other, in a refined way, about their evergreens.

The man with the hand-painted tie, who had left the hose running on his best specimens and hoped his wife would remember to move it, owned an even fifty of them—seventy-five, if you counted the two-year-old transplants he was raising in the nursery row.

The man with the long cigarette holder had only twenty-six, but they were big and dense, having been kept on a rigid pruning schedule; and they included two specimens of Carolina hemlock, and two gold-tipped, ball-shaped arborvitae. It sounded as if, on a quality basis, or a cubic-foot basis, or a tonsorial basis, he might be ahead.

Eventually, perhaps, Dun and Bradstreet may list a man's evergreen status. As a criterion of success, it seems to be finding popular acceptance, especially in landscapes from which Nature long ago eliminated the evergreen.

189

The conversation had started with an appraisal of the plantings around that Chicago airport, where the inevitable competition was evident, between man's choice of plant material and Nature's choice. About man's choice there was no question. It was evergreens and tailored lawn. But Nature had other ideas, raggedly informal—such ideas as the native pioneers, cottonwood and box-elder; or the foreign camp followers, ailanthus trees and dandelions.

How long would it be, I wondered, before that seedling cotton-wood would be discovered by the authorities, trespassing there between the Pfitzer junipers and the arborvitae; or that vigorous ailanthus sapling that had pre-empted the angle in the concrete wall as its universally established domain.

Then a woman with an orchid breasted up to the fence just beyond the two conifer-proprietors.

The orchid's dramatic lower petal was extended with a receptive gesture. Flowers certainly offer more decorative landing places than airlines do, I thought, as I looked at that extraordinary threshold that the orchid holds out to insects.

That particular orchid offered a landing place like sculptured purple marble inlaid with lines of gold that converged at the luminous portal to the business section of the flower. But the glamorous structure was not functioning, except as a badge of solvency, like the brief-casers' evergreens.

As I tore my eyes away from the orchid, I saw yet another landing place, a lowly one. There was a dandelion blooming in a crack at the edge of the cement runway. It appeared to be function-ing; at least, a fly was on it, apparently drinking. Whether or not he was paying for his drink by delivering pollen, I could not see, and November was hardly the time for maturing seeds, anyhow.

That landing place was as different from the orchid's pastel colored one, as the entrance to Coney Island is different from a vaulted portal with a purple wedding carpet laid before it—and as much more likely to lead to vigorous, abundant progeny.

The dandelion was holding its nectar in shallow goblets, not too deep for the tongues of numerous insects. Its presence was advertised by a color visible to the partially color-blind bee, a color conspicuous in the sunlight. Its form was as economical of expenditure for display as the orchid's form was spendthrift. The dandelion was composed of many flowers, a hundred or more, packed tightly into a head, and pooling their expenditure on stem and petal material.

And each of these yellow flowers makes only one seed, while the orchid (if its elaborately specialized pollination mechanism has an opportunity for functioning) makes thousands and thousands of seeds. Here the tables are turned—now the orchid, so spendthrift of advertising and allure, proves niggardly in its seed-packaging. Each little embryo plant starts out with such a meager endowment of food that its chances for survival are slight. But the dandelion's embryo is provisioned with a supply of food adequate to give it a bounding start in life.

The lasting qualities of these two landing places speak, too, of their individual problems. The orchid, poised on a branch in a steamy atmosphere, needs to last a long time while it awaits the languid, fluttering approach of the pollinating visitor that may not come for many days. But the dandelion, pioneering in earth's wounds, has many a bustling visitor hurtling in to drink. It requires no durable substance. No wonder the orchid rides the perfumed pearl-gray lapel and mink, while the dandelion gets the dust of the runway blown across its face.

Then the DC3 was ready. It lifted us, orchid, brief cases, and all, up over back yards and alleys that are the fouled nests of humans, and over the unyielding geometry of the industrial districts, where Nature's only opportunity for shaping curves is the smoke.

From Chicago to Dayton, we looked down on a battle, the battle between man's passion for square corners and Nature's penchant for curves.

Across one stretch of country the grid of lines was so accurate, the lines so straight, that I thought that the terrain down there must be as flat as a billiard table, until I noticed that the shadow of our plane was riding humps down there.

It was not only the roads that made squares. The rivets on the wing of the plane were a geometric pattern riding over that other geometric pattern down below—a pattern made of fields, and fences, corn rows, wood lots, orchard rows, cemetery plots, and lines of plowing and mowing and irrigation, and sidewalks and driveways of city subdivisions—so uniform that they looked like products of a punch press.

Under this net, Nature was squirming and resisting.

She was scrawling a meandering stream zigzag across the ritual of straight lines. And where a farmer had turned his back for a moment, she was rubbing a thumb across and blurring the precision of impeccable fence rows with a welter of hawthorns, wild plums, and wild roses. It was easy to identify the hawthorns from the DC3. There is no mistaking the gray foam of them. And the rest of the fraternity inevitably comes along when the hawthorn invades the fence row.

In one place the farmer's fence had been shifted slightly by an undermining gully.

It could be seen, from this height, that Nature was tampering even with the over-all pattern of man's wheat and rye fields, by overlaying the flat squares with a dappled marbling that was sheet erosion.

The pattern of the square is a rare one in living things. Flowers are most often five-parted, less often three-parted, and seldom four-parted. It is true, there are some four-parted ones: the mustards, poppies, and olives are in fours; and the mints have square stems, as do the blue ash and usually the euonymus. But even these squares are softened by flowing contours.

The spiral appears over and over again: in the center of a sunflower head; in the outward corkscrewing of a twig; in the downward thrust of a root tip; in the ascent of a vine. The circle and the five-pointed star are often repeated, the triangle, too. But not the square.

Just when it seemed as if man's geometry was everywhere an alien temporary mold that had nothing in common with Nature's lines, just then we noticed paths, footpaths that crossed fields near the edge of town, or made a short cut to a country school or a cross-roads community.

These little paths ambled and sauntered. They swung out into curves for no apparent reason. But there must have been a rise of ground, or a depression at each curve, not visible from the air.

Cow paths, too, followed the contour.

Then we saw a country road, dark-colored, with edges that were blurred probably by elderberry, blackberry, bittersweet. It ambled and curved like the little paths. It wandered through a small town, and then, abruptly, it straightened with a jerk, and cut like a gash across a large town. As it entered the outskirts of the large town, it passed close to an area marked by a snarl of exaggeratedly curveting roads and sidewalks, with dark masses of evergreens. That must have been Suburbia.

It occurred to me that there, in the life story of a road, just as in the story of a filling lake, or the story of a dune, or a bog, the vertical and the horizontal successions would be the same. A barefoot boy might follow a deer path through the woods, among lady ferns, trilliums, sugar maples; he might continue on as the path became wider, with a plank laid down here and there; he might find himself presently on a dirt road; and then he might be walking on a cement sidewalk beside a paved street; and finally he might find that the sidewalk ran close beside the pavement on the one side and beside the front of a building on the other, while fireplugs and newsstands grew where lady ferns had been. That would be the "horizontal succession." But, if he had the time, he could stand perfectly still on the deer path, and simply wait until the same changes came to the path. It might take a long time. It might all happen within a lifetime, but if the deer path lay near a growing town the changes would come eventually. That would be the "vertical succession."

There are aspects of the land that are revealed to the air traveler, though they are seldom seen otherwise.

The shame of many a farmer, for example, is laid bare. Gullies, far from the public road, and heretofore hidden from the passer-by, are all too apparent from the air. It will be interesting to see whether the spotlight of public scrutiny will have an effect on these indecent scrawls.

Another thing revealed from the air was bee-hives, long white rows of them. They looked like sugar cubes along the end of an orchard in one place, ambling beside a brook in another, and strung out along the edge of an open field in another.

Then we began to notice differences in the occasional stretches of woods beneath us. There were many woodlands that were transparent right down to the ground. Those were evidently the ones that had been grazed, or perhaps burned over each spring. Probably both, because the same kind of farmer that allows his woods to be grazed is likely to burn them over too.

There were woods that were not grazed. We could not look down through those,—even though November had stripped all but the white oaks of their leaves. It was easy to understand that raindrops, dropping from our viewpoint and passing through that layered vegetation, would be broken and broken again, until they sank, captured, into the leaf mold. But on the grazed forest, where seedlings and shrubs and saplings had been eliminated, raindrops would hammer down with a gouging force; the few raspberries and thistles would not break their force enough to matter.

Those grazed forests would be gone, soon, unable to reproduce themselves in the face of the cows.

We looked down on many planted wood lots. Almost all of them were as accurately squared lots as the rest of the scenery. I wondered how many of those farmers knew about the interesting piece of research on bird population that had been done by the Academy of Sciences in Chicago(1). If they knew about the evidence that bird population varies directly as the amount of edge on a forest, they would surely feel inclined to work some scallops, bays, peninsulas, onto the edges of those wood lots, and double their bird population.

THE STORY OF A ROAD

From woodland path to city street, natives are gradually replaced by foreigners

First—a foot path

with sugar maple, lady ferns, trilliums, ovenbirds, foxes

Soon—a country lane

with hawthorn, wild plum, bracken fern, violets, brown thrasher, woodchuck

Presently—a country road

with apple trees, white pine, elderberry, rabbits, wild strawberry, meadow larks

Then—the edge of the country

with silver maple, Norway maple, Norway spruce, dandelion, robin, deer mouse

Then—the edge of the city

with cottonwood, catalpa, box elder, plantain, starling, house mouse

Finally—the city

with tree of heaven, English sparrow, Norway rat, pigeons, German cockroach, African violet

We landed at South Bend. The evergreens were neat. So was the grass. The dandelions, cottonwood seedlings, and an ailanthus tree were doing their bit toward blurring the man-made straight edges.

At Fort Wayne, Indiana, we made another landing. The evergreens, grass, dandelions, and cottonwoods were there, too—and a few ungainly box-elders.

We left the plane at Dayton, and walked over to the bus, past dandelions, grass, clipped evergreens, and an invading ailanthus tree.

REFERENCES

1. *Nesting Birds and the Vegetation Substrata* by William J. Beecher. Chicago Ornithological Society, Chicago, 1942.
2. *Hedgerows* by Nicholas Drahos, *Cornell Rural School Leaflet* **40** (Fall, 1946), Number 2.
3. *Pleasant Valley,* by Louis Bromfield. Harper, New York, 1945.
4. *Bees: Their Vision, Chemical Senses, and Language,* by Karl von Frisch. Cornell University Press, Ithaca, New York, 1950.
5. "A Comparison of Reproductive Potential in Two Rat Populations" by David E. Davis. *Ecology* **32** (July, 1951), 469-475.
6. "Controlled Burning—Its Broader Ecological Aspects," by John E. Cantlon and Murray F. Buell. *Bartonia* **26** (December, 1952), 48-52.

13.

THE STYLISH HOUSE

or

Fashions as an Ecological Factor

THIS is going to be an account of a certain old house, and the plants in its life.

There has been a definite succession of these plants; and the major ecological force in determining this succession has been *style*.

This old house has always belonged to stylish people. Always stylish, never queer. (No doubt the present owners would, with a shudder, substitute "smart" for "stylish," and "unadjusted" for "queer," and that is in character.)

Everyone knows this house, or its counterpart—everyone who knows midwestern towns, at any rate.

It is two blocks, uphill from the bank corner, on the "good" side of the tracks, on the street with the tallest elms.

Jonathan and Patience were the dignified names of the first owners, and their dog was a collie named Rover.

The first thing that Jonathan planted was a white pine tree, on the southwest corner of the lot. That was in 1856. He bought the pine from a traveling nurseryman, who put a nose bag on his horse and stayed to lunch himself; and he had a beard, as Jonathan did, too. He was inclined to be skeptical about the virtues of used tea leaves as a stimulant for plants. But that was what Patience used just the same, and it certainly seemed to agree with the pine tree.

The first things that Patience planted were the Harison's yellow rose in the front yard and the cabbage rose against the board fence. She had brought slips of those along from Ohio. They did well out in the full sun. The lilies of the valley, that she planted against the east side of the stone basement, throve, too, and spread so that she was able to give roots to newcomers in the Ladies' Aid at church, just as they had been given to her.

The ostrich fern and the lady fern were brought back from the Sunday School picnic out at Sugar Grove, and planted against the basement on the north side.

There was a russet apple tree, a sweet bough, a maiden blush, a damson plum, a Richmond cherry, raspberries and grapes. Jonathan had bought those along with the white pine, and the elms beside the hitching post.

The box-elder out behind the barn came of its own accord. So did the ailanthus tree back of the outhouse, and the wild plum inside the chicken yard, and the big elderberry in the back fence corner.

Patience planted the gourds on the trellis in front of the outhouse door, and the two rows of tawny day-lilies along the path to the outhouse. "Privy lilies," her friend down the street called them as she dug up the roots for Patience, from among those beside her own outhouse path.

The flower bed was a long straight stretch along the board fence. Hollyhocks bloomed in it, and a red fern-leaved peony, and sweet Williams, pinks, feverfew, Johnny-jump-ups, and yellow irises ("flags," Patience called them). In the spring there were blue squills. The children always used a few of those with the lily of the valley, and some hepaticas from the woods, when they made their May baskets to hang on doorknobs.

Jonathan kept up the bed of mint, the rhubarb, the asparagus, raspberries, and the big vegetable garden down back of the barn, where he was considering experimenting with some of those new tomatoes, having read of the success that plant breeders were having with increasing the size of the fruit and taking out the wrinkles.

Plants prospered. There was plenty of horse manure, and chicken manure, and wood ashes. When Jonathan went fishing, he could find plenty of plump earthworms in the garden.

The grass was scythed, and the horse was tethered out on it occasionally.

There were no massed shrubs for privacy. Jonathan and Patience wanted to see who was passing when they heard horses on the dirt road. But there were two white lilacs beside the front gate, and two great shrubs set in the middle of the side lawn. One was a snowball bush. The other was a sweet shrub. Patience used to tie one of its mahogany-colored flowers in the corner of her little daughter's handkerchief on Sunday, to help her through the sermon by letting her smell its fragrance of crushed strawberries.

The yard was quiet, except for the sound of horses passing, and an occasional rooster, or church bell, or a boy holding a stick against a picket fence as he ran by.

Inside the house, the sound of the grandfather clock was loud, and there was the smell of baking bread, wood smoke, and kerosene lamps.

Red geraniums bloomed between the lace curtains of the front windows, and in the dining-room bay window, and in the kitchen, too, where the air was rich and steamy, with no gas. A huge Boston fern backed up the geraniums in the dining room, and near it Patience was coddling a cutting from her neighbor's Christmas cactus.

In the front parlor wax flowers stood stiffly under a glass dome, on a marble-topped table, under the picture of Pharaoh's Horses, and between the big family Bible and the stereoscope.

Flowers lay flat within the Bible, too—pressed ones, representing memorable moments: lily of the valley from a wedding bouquet, Queen Anne's lace from a moonlit surrey ride, a pansy from a christening, and a four-leaf clover or two.

On the corner of the melodeon, beside the hymn book, under the "Stag at Bay" by Sir Edwin Landseer, a pink luster vase sometimes held a tight little nosegay known as a tussy-mussy. Rose geranium leaves encircled the tussy-mussy, and it usually contained mignonette and pinks, and a little lemon-verbena.

Roses in several forms graced the front parlor. A red rose was embroidered in gleaming silk on the round black cushion that stood upright on the horsehair sofa under the picture of "Breaking Home Ties," and a big pink rose flowered on the hooked welcome mat. And on the white marble mantel in the back parlor there was a rose jar filled with a potpourri from the cabbage roses in the yard.

There were roses in the dining room, too, mixed with daisies and forget-me-nots, on the cross-stitch sampler with "God Bless Our Home."

Sometimes Patience would put a rose into one of the pieces from her collection of china hands—the one with the two slender hands upheld to form a vase. But if she put it on the table, the menfolks seemed to find it in the way of the caster and the spoonholder, the accepted occupants of the center of the table.

More roses were on the shade of the hanging lamp with the crystal pendants.

There was a rose on the sampler over the spool bed in the bedroom. But the doily under the pitcher and washbowl on the commode was embroidered with silken violets.

Jonathan and Patience had six children, named David, John, Paul, Daniel, Ruth, and Rachel, after Biblical characters.

When the eldest son, David, brought his bride, Mary, home to live, some changes were made. That was in 1881.

The board fence was taken down, since there was no longer much danger of a stray wandering cow. A stout wooden fence topped with big wooden balls was substituted.

One day David had to cut down the big old snowball bush. In its place he made a circular bed.

On Sunday afternoons, when David and Mary went for their walk around town after dinner, to work up an appetite for an early supper —early so that they could wash the dishes before evening service, and get to bed extra early because Monday was washday—they looked at other people's circular flower beds. So they planted red cannas in the center, encircled by nasturtiums, with a final edging of dwarf blue lobelias.

With the snowball bush gone, the sweet shrub looked wrong, standing there in the center of the lawn, so they took it out, and made another circular bed. In this one they planted castor beans, encircled by red geraniums and outlined with sweet alyssum.

These gay beds were so much admired that David and Mary

decided to outdo themselves for the ice-cream sociable, which was to be held in their yard under strings of Japanese lanterns.

First they planted a weeping mulberry in the side yard. Then they formed a big star-shaped bed around it. The center was massed

with red cockscombs. Each point of the star was filled with golden-foliaged coleus, and outlined with variegated-leaved coleus. Then the whole was outlined with hen and chickens.

Then they put in the fountain—the one with the little girl and boy under the iron umbrella, with water shooting out of the tip of the umbrella and dripping down the sides into a little circular pool. The pool was surrounded by green-and-white-leaved plantain lily, encircled by abalone shells side by side, with one edge thrust into the ground so that they made an upright pearly scalloping.

The garden really looked like an embroidery piece under the Japanese lanterns, especially so since the lawn was clipped more closely now, with the new lawn mower.

Later, when the strawberry sociable was held on the lawn of another home, David and Mary admired the iron deer, and the iron dog standing guard over a sleeping iron child, but they really envied the new decorations on the house itself, the scroll-saw work made possible by new machinery.

They decided to have some, and before the house was painted (yellow), they had its edges embellished with wooden tatting, and the corners filled out with scallops and eyelet embroidery in wood.

They built a porch out over the front stoop. It covered the set-back door with its side lights, but it made room for more scroll-saw work, and the two posts could hold porch boxes.

There was no question about what to plant in the center of each porch box, that was established—*Dracaena indivisa*, for a stiff upright element. There was no question, either, about the lower masses at the base of the stiff dracaena. They were pink geraniums (redness was having a tendency to leach out of the possessions of Mary and her friends). But there was some choice in the matter of the drooping material to drizzle over the edges. One might choose asparagus fern, or coleus, or variegated vinca. Mary mixed them.

Somehow, during the installation of the scroll-saw work, the crimson rambler on the side porch died. Mary planted a pink Dorothy Perkins instead.

David liked to build. He put up a grape arbor across the end of the vegetable garden, with a pleasant seat where Mary liked to shell peas or string beans. And he built a peaked roof over the pump, and put a wind vane on the barn, when they took the lightning rod down.

They had only half as many chickens as Jonathan and Patience had kept, but they used the extra space to make a paddock for the horse, now that the nearby field was no longer available for pasture.

And there was a dog run, for the airedale, now that the garden was so trim, lest he blur the corner of some star or crescent.

When Mary brought her flowers into the house, she did not pack them so tightly into the vases and bowls as Patience had done, and she left more leaves on the stems. The flowers she favored were the globular, thoroughly double ones.

In the dining room she massed zinnias in a cut-glass bowl on the sideboard beside the chafing dish. The silver fern dish was usually in the center of the dining-room table on a crocheted doily.

In the parlor she put a vase of round red dahlias on the organ that had replaced the melodeon there against the wall where the crayon portraits of Jonathan and Patience had replaced the "Stag at Bay." (Later, when the children insisted on having the parlor organ replaced by a player piano, the crayon portraits were replaced by the "Song of the Lark," and presently "Pharaoh's Horses" was replaced by a tinted photograph of the Rheims Cathedral.

"Breaking Home Ties" had been the first of the old pictures to go. It went out with Patience's horsehair and walnut furniture, when the new three-piece golden-oak suite was bought from the mail-order catalogue, along with the Brussels carpet.

Geraniums no longer throve in the windows, after the gas was installed. But there was a rubber plant in one window and an umbrella plant in another. Even without the gas, the geraniums would probably not have thriven as they did in Patience's day, because the window hangings were now of heavy stuff with a fringe of red balls. They shut out the light, but they matched the heavy portieres, and the velvet cushions of the Morris chair in the cosy corner.

In the bedroom Mary sometimes put a bowl of pansies on the bamboo table where she kept the "Ben Hur" that she was going to read on top of the "East Lynn" that she was reading. Over the big double brass bed, with the spread embroidered in lazy-daisy stitch and French knots, hung several pictures of the Gibson Girl, upon whom Mary's appearance was patterned. David's was patterned on the Gibson Man, to such an extent that he finally shaved off his curving mustaches, and took to wearing those padded shoulders in his coats.

Out in the kitchen the geraniums had moved from the window sills to the curtains, where they were embroidered. The new gas range caused that change.

The dining-room geraniums had moved, too—onto the hand-painted china plates along the plate rail. A mother-in-law's tongue and ivy took the place of the geraniums in the bay window.

In spring, when Mary brought the first bunch of lilies of the valley into the house, their fragrance no longer mingled with the smell of kerosene lamps and wood smoke. The new furnace, one of the first in town, smoked only a little. But there was still the smell of new-baked bread and simmering soup.

When David sat in the Morris chair in his smoking jacket on winter evenings, and read seed catalogues, he saw the first pictures of the new sweet corn. Mary read about the regal lily that E. H. Wilson had brought home for gardens from the alpine meadows of Tibet, and the butterfly bush, and the beauty bush.

Mary and David had four children, named Theodore, Ethel, Victoria, and Charles. The names were taken from the Teddy Roosevelt family, the Queen of England, and Dickens.

When Theodore and his young wife Elizabeth (named after Beth in "Little Women") decided to take down the picket fence, they did it partly to be "neighborly." Everyone else was doing it, too. That was the influence of the realtors, who were subdividing big corner lots like this one into smaller plots for bungalows and who needed to have places look, at least until sold, more spacious than they actually were.

But after a few years of crisscross paths on the lawn showed that corner lots make a good short cut, Theodore and Elizabeth began to put back a barrier. Everyone else was doing that, too. The fences themselves were not put back, but small plantings that could be counted on to grow rapidly and insinuate themselves into the scene without being abruptly unneighborly.

A barberry hedge was the solution that Theodore and Elizabeth chose. Most people did, although a few chose privet.

At about that time, Elizabeth began to read gardening hints in the *Ladies' Home Journal.* She found out about foundation planting. Simultaneously she found out about bridal wreath, *Spiraea Van*

Houttei. Soon the high house was set afloat in a billowing sea of bridal wreath. No slightest contact with the earth was visible, except at the steps of course, where a gap was necessary.

Then Theodore learned about the popular demand for Lombardy poplars that was making them hard to get. So he managed to get some, and planted a row along the fence.

With a house so abreast of the times as to be embowered in bridal wreath, ringed with barberry hedge, and edged with a row of

Lombardy poplars, it was to be expected that Elizabeth would be invited to join the new garden club.

At her very first meeting she learned that David and Mary's round beds in the center of the lawn were "wrong." The centers must be kept open, to create a sweep of lawn, a "vista." She learned that straight lines and scallops were out. Flowing, "naturalistic" curves were in.

There came a lady lecturer who told the garden club members to go home and get out their garden hoses, but not for sprinkling. They were to lay down the hoses to shape the edges of their borders, and then dig to follow those natural curves.

Elizabeth did it. So did her neighbors. She never spoke of her "garden" again. She spoke of her "borders."

Everything was wide open with flowing margins.

Presently the garden club had a lecture on rock gardens. The magazines were full of rock gardens, too.

The instructions said to bury two thirds of each rock in the soil. But by the time Theodore and Elizabeth had broken the springs on their Ford carrying home rocks from all over the country, they could not bear to conceal two thirds of that carefully selected mass.

They constructed a sort of pinnacle, with a suggestion of a grotto about it. On this pinnacle they planted a lot of *Alyssum saxatile*, basket of gold: *Phlox subulata;* maidenhair fern; thyme; winter aconite; pinks; and one *Daphne cneorum*, and one Christmas rose.

The yellow alyssum and the pink phlox lived, and so did a few of the hen-and-chicken plants that Elizabeth had saved from the edging of Mary's star-shaped bed.

In her flowing borders, Elizabeth specialized on big brilliant zinnias—at first. But later she heard so much about subtle coloring at the garden club, that she eschewed red flowers, regretfully because Theodore seemed to like them.

She was veering toward pastel shades. She had memorized the hint that one did not approve of magenta, but was not quite certain about what that color looked like.

She was planting in "drifts," instead of in rows or masses, and always planting three or five or seven of a kind.

Having an automobile instead of a horse brought about some changes in the yard. The ailanthus tree and the box-elder were cut down after they had dented fenders on the car. There was no longer abundant manure for the garden. Theodore missed that because he was growing the new Golden Bantam corn, and Kentucky Wonder pole beans, and a row of giant dahlias. Elizabeth missed it because she was turning away from annuals to perennials, and had decided to specialize on delphiniums.

When the chickens were finally given up, there was room for a sandbox and a lawn swing, and a basket for basketball practice was attached to the barn. There was a dog run, too, for the wire-haired fox terriers.

When Elizabeth picked flowers for the house, she planned them carefully for different rooms. On the round pedestal table in the dining room, she put a low loose mass in soft pastel tones. *Delphinium belladonna*, with baby's breath and Rosy Morn petunias, was a favorite; or love-in-a-mist with salmon-rose zinnias, in a green pottery bowl.

In the living room she arranged marigolds, or sunflowers, in a bean pot on the monk's cloth runner on the new black mission table that had replaced the golden oak. It stood beside the blue plush over-stuffed chair under the Maxfield Parrish picture with the very-blue sky, that had replaced the Rheims Cathedral. ("The Song of the Lark" had been replaced by a picture of "Old Ironsides," and the crayon portraits by Whistler's "Mother.")

Elizabeth did not pick flowers for the new upright piano. She dusted the dried bouquet there, carefully, because she had spent a lot of time, first out in the fields looking for the big curled-up leaves of the prairie dock, and then painting them silver and bronze. It had taken time, too, to dip the milkweed pods in silver paint, and then tint the inside of each one a bright orange. They stood in a black vase, with three silvered Osage oranges lying casually at the base, on the random folds of a fringed and embroidered Oriental shawl that was draped across one corner of the piano.

In the bedroom, Elizabeth sometimes slipped a pansy or two under the plate-glass cover of the chiffonier, where stood the two big tinted photographs of their children, Kathryn Jane and John Edward, in silver frames, flanking the silver-backed comb and brush set. And she put one rose bud into the bud vase on the table between the twin beds with the blue silk spreads. The bud vase stood between the "A Girl of the Limberlost" that Elizabeth was reading, which was covered by the Carl Sandburg poems that she intended to read; and "The Call of the Wild" that Theodore was reading, which was covered by H. G. Wells's "Outline of History" that he intended to read.

Elizabeth did not have many house plants, except for Mary's Christmas cactus in the dining-room bay window, and a small-flowered pink begonia. But there was an abundance of flowers, thoroughly naturalistic, on the cretonne drapes at most of the windows. And the trailing bunch of bittersweet that was placed in the pottery wall pocket each fall had a way of lasting most of the year.

When Theodore and Elizabeth read seed catalogues in the winter evenings, they sat on the side porch, which was a glassed-in sun parlor now, with steam heat and wicker furniture. There were Boston ferns in the wicker fernery, and a little green plant of cabomba in the fish bowl. And on the cretonne drapes and table runners and slip covers and pillows were big magnolia blossoms and parrots. Elizabeth started her flats of seedlings out there in the spring.

The new vegetables in the catalogues interested Theodore—New Zealand spinach and Chinese celery cabbage; while Elizabeth read about the tall English delphiniums.

When John Edward and his young wife, Nancy Ann, took over the old house, one of their first purchases was a pair of pruning shears—which, unfortunately, then as now, could be purchased without a license. Then John Edward proceeded to give his shrubs prison haircuts.

It didn't matter whether their charm was in arching sprays or in rugged gesture—they all emerged from the pruning with identical globular, twiggy forms. Even the billows of the foundation bridal wreath were transformed into leggy knobs.

This was neat.

At first the neatness pleased John Edward and Nancy Ann, but gradually the appearance began to bother them. The bare high stone foundation of the old house showed plainly between the shorn, leggy shrubs. Nancy Ann and John Edward looked at the other high old houses around the town. They found out what was being done.

First they had a terrace built, to cover the foundation. But the house still looked a little naked to them.

Then they went to a neighboring nurseryman. He came and looked at the house, but really he knew, before he looked, just what the prescription would be—evergreens. At each side of the front door he set a dwarf Mugho pine. Behind that he set a Pfitzer juniper, backed up by a red cedar. Around the foundation he used the prevalent "dot and dash system"—one high, one low, one high, one low.

Nancy Ann, at the garden club, had been relieved of her fear of straight lines. The taboo had been lifted. So the borders had been straightened out somewhat.

She had decided to specialize in hybrid tea roses. A sunken rose garden was worked out. The extra dirt was used to build up the terrace. But the terrace operations had broken up a part of the cement walk. They took it all up, broke it into random chunks, and laid it down again, flagstone style.

Nancy Ann decided that the walk should have a wide curve in it. But after the new curved walk was already laid, and after she had sprinkled portulaca seeds between the flags, the garden club had a lecturer who was quite merry on the subject of walks that had a curve when no obstacle necessitated it.

It developed that a walk must not curve unless there was something for it to curve around, but that it was quite within the rules of the game to plant the obstacle first, and then detour around it, or to plant it afterwards even, in the hope that it would appear to have been there first.

John Edward and Nancy Ann
1931
to
1941
Bee
Chuck
and
Lassie

For the obstacle that was seemingly to have necessitated Nancy's curve, the nurseryman suggested the very thing that John Edward and Nancy Ann had been planning to add to their plantings, in some conspicuous position—a Colorado spruce. They bought one of the exceptionally blue ones.

The Lombardy poplars had been winterkilled. The barberry hedge caught every passing bit of paper, and Nancy Ann wanted a

211

white picket fence anyhow. The gate that they installed was a wagon wheel that Nancy Ann found at a second-hand dealer's.

It all had a quite quaint look, especially after the old lamppost was installed in front of the blue spruce, and after they set up the humorous old Negro-boy hitching post, and the flamingo and a duck family.

John Edward was having a little trouble with his vegetables. There was no manure any more, except for a rare load when some farmer could be talked into delivering it. When John Edward tried to dig worms for the children's fishing, they proved scarce and rather lean. But he learned that other people were using chemical fertilizers freely on their gardens. So he tried them too. They seemed to work.

He had lost a part of the vegetable-garden area to Nancy's herb garden. Losing the space didn't bother him so much as eating the herbs. Parsley, mint, and chives, he was accustomed to. It was the basil in his lemonade; the bee balm in his tea; the marjoram in the pot roast; and the thyme in the chicken dressing, that he could have done without. Nancy Ann liked to try out these things. She even put great heads of elderberry blossoms into the pancakes one Sunday morning in June, but the pancakes tasted almost as good as usual, so John Edward put on a little more butter and syrup and didn't mind much.

The mountain ash and white birch had long since died as a result of borers. John Edward asked the nursery for something fast-growing to give shade on the lawn. Siberian elms were recommended. They were inexpensive so he bought six. Four of them were used, clipped into lollipop shape, one at each side of the two openings through the privet hedge into the sunken rose garden.

From the rose garden one could catch a glimpse of an old well sweep. Nancy Ann had bought that at an auction, and used it, as a lecturer had suggested, to disguise the incinerator.

But it did not stay there long. John Edward objected to being lured, by the suggestion of coolness and depth, to look down into half-burned orange peels. Nancy traded it to a neighbor, who filled the well curb with geraniums, and the bucket with balcony petunias. The neighbor gave Nancy two statues of elves, in exchange. They were placed in the shrubbery so that they peered out where least expected.

Out near the garage, where the old lawn swing had been, John Edward put up a fireplace and built picnic tables.

The garden began to lose the pastel effect of Elizabeth's time. Nancy went in for white. White petunias took the place of Rosy Morn. White delphiniums stood tall beside Madonna lilies. Silver-leaved plants were used freely. Agrostemma, dusty miller, artemisia, Russian olive, were favorites.

The flowers that Nancy brought into the house were usually white, now that the interior decorator had done the living room in silver and London fog.

The piano (it was a parlor grand, but seldom played because of interfering with radio programs) made a dramatic setting for a large mass of white peonies, or silver-poplar leaves. On the gray table, Nancy put Shasta daisies in a pewter tankard, below the ranks of etchings that had replaced Maxfield Parrish. Old Ironsides, and Whistler's Mother were gone, too, replaced by a Currier and Ives print, above the spinning wheel; and a page from Godey's Lady's Book, near the rush-bottomed spindle-backed chairs and the ship model.

Nancy Ann had a dried winter bouquet made of the silver moons of honesty, combined with Artemisia Silver King.

On the dining-room table Nancy arranged white roses, or white chrysanthemums, and five rhododendron leaves, asymmetrically in a low oyster-colored container, set on a mirror.

In the bedroom there was no room for flowers on the table between the spool beds with candlewick spreads, because the radio filled the place between "Gone With the Wind" under Robert Frost's poems, on Nancy's side, and "The Grapes of Wrath" under Toynbee, on John Edward's side. But there was a chaste flower print over each bed.

Nancy Ann favored miniature house plants. At one time she had a Japanese dish garden with tiny figures of ladies and herons and bridges, but she gave that up in favor of a cactus collection, which she arranged on glass shelves against the window pane. The cactus plants and other succulents were planted in quaint, often humorous, containers—elephants, dachshunds, ducks, and penguins.

She had a terrarium, too, pear-shaped, with partridgeberries and selaginella in it. She decided against joining some of her friends in their hobby of making arrangements on buttons.

John Edward and Nancy Ann had a Doberman pinscher, and two children, called Bee and Chuck.

Their stay in the old house was a short one—people weren't staying so long anywhere any more. In 1941 they moved out of town. Kathryn Jane, John Edward's sister, and her husband, Don, took over.

When Don and Kathryn Jane (she was called "Kay") looked over the grounds, they decided to enlarge the terrace to fit the height of the house. Then they took up the walk of broken concrete. They laid down a new straight walk of brick, in a herringbone pattern. Before they could get rid of Nancy Ann's curve, they had to move the blue spruce. It went over into the side lines, where it was presently joined by other displaced specimens.

The first plants to join the spruce did so as a result of a session of the new garden club, composed of men and women both, and meeting in the evening.

Don and Kay both attended that meeting, and learned with surprise that now, after the years of struggle to cover foundations stylishly, it was smart to reveal the fact that a house rested on the ground. They learned that corners were being planted, and entrances, but that the rest of the ground line was being left naked.

After a decent period of adjustment, they began moving the surviving units of the "dot and dash" period, over to join the blue spruce.

To replace the Mugho-Pfitzer-cedar combination at the front door, they planted two Hicks yews. They covered the ground at the base of the yews with Baltic ivy and planted white tulips in the ivy. For the corners of the house they chose spreading yews.

Arborvitae from the former foundation planting came in handy when Don and Kay learned about having a main axis in the garden, terminating at a focal point. They decided to feature the path from the house through the rose garden. At the end of this path they placed an oval pool, backed by a clump of arborvitae. Against this dark background they placed a statue of "St. Francis Feeding the Birds."

Soon afterward there was a hard winter that left the old privet hedge around the rose garden marred with dead patches. Don and Kay learned that there were other hedge materials besides privet and barberry. They replaced the privet with a low trimmed hedge of Japanese quince, knowing that its ribbon of color would be past its blooming before the roses brought uncongenial shades. An ice storm that winter broke up the Siberian elms. Don planted a thornless honey locust.

At the garden fair where they bought St. Francis, Kay saw a display of white iron furniture and a glass-topped table. She began at once to plan for a place that would do justice to such equipment.

So they paved an area under the old apple tree, using blue slate. There they set out the iron furniture, and also a chaise longue with a pale-green waterproof cushion.

Presently they decided to take out, or at least, to interrupt, the long line of Tartarian honeysuckle. There were two reasons for this decision. The first reason was that they wanted their backgrounds to have interest of varied combinations of texture, color, and irregular profile. The second reason was that word was going around that some of our native plants have more to offer in the way of both grace and hardihood than some of the European plants that had dominated gardens for so long a time.

Don and Kay added wild plum, wild crab, hawthorn, shadbush, witch-hazel, nannyberry, aronia, prairie rose, and New Jersey tea, to their plantings. They developed a natural-looking bit of thicket out of these native shrubs and small trees, and wove a tanbark path through the thicket. In spring the path was bordered with mertensia, wild ginger, and wild phlox. In the summer there were lady fern, leather wood fern, and jewelweed.

Don and Kay used considerable peat moss on this and other plantings. And then, one evening, they had a lecturer at the garden club who talked about compost piles. In fact he practically divided humanity into two classes—those who have compost piles and those who do not. Don and Kay decided to join the new compost-pile aristocracy.

The compost pile gave Don and Kay the same feeling of respect-

216

ability that Jonathan and Patience had obtained from their white pine tree.

Kay was all ready to send away for a package of earthworms, when Don happened to discover that their own compost was practically teeming with them.

Don gave compost offerings to the old white pine, the old apple tree, the bleeding heart, and the fern-leaved peony—the same plants that had been fed tea leaves by Patience, fresh manure by David, nothing by Theodore, and commercial fertilizer by Nancy Ann. They continued to thrive.

Kay used a lot of the compost for her new venture—tuberous begonias, out on the shady side of the barn.

The end of the barn had been converted into a garden house, but the garden-house end was gradually changing into a studio, now that Don had taken up painting.

Don was experimenting with roses too. He owned an expensive array of sprays and fertilizers. He was hearing rumors of the wisdom of dispensing with these through the use of organic fertilizers only. But that far he was not ready to go.

In her flower garden Kay did not favor white flowers so much as Nancy Ann had, nor did she lean to the pastel shades as Elizabeth had. She planned her garden with a color chart, and chose analogous colors, rather than the complementary colors so long in favor. She liked such combinations as deep purple and clear blue.

When she picked flowers to bring into the house, she struck poses that fascinated Don. She would rear up, tilt her head back, squint her eyes, and sketch Hogarth's curve of beauty in the air with her clippers. Then she would ignore the lush, fulsome flower cluster that would have delighted Patience, and choose a tortured asymmetrical spray. From this, she proceeded to remove any leaves that interfered with the gesture, or movement, or flow of line, or mood. Sometimes all of them interfered.

She plunged her trophies deep in pails of water and took them down to the basement. The ritual of arrangement would come after they were thoroughly soaked, "hardened."

She had picked every specimen with a definite container, position, and background in mind. Since the woman's garden club had become practically an arrangement society, she knew all the latest rules—all that had been formulated up until the time of the last club meeting, at any rate.

First she made an arrangement for the marble-topped table in the living room. She had discovered that table in an antique shoppe. (It was an exact counterpart of the carved walnut table that Patience had had in the same position, and that Mary had sold off when her golden-oak suite arrived. It may have been the same table.)

Kay selected a low off-white bowl. At one end she arranged three sprays of weeping willow. She was careful to see that they soared to carry the motion rhythmically up and around, and then back to the bowl. She never failed to check the tips of the twigs to see whether an imaginary drip from them would fall back into the container. The flower-arrangement lecturers seemed to stress that point. At the base of the willow a little green Buddha squatted, and a few petals of a pale salmon poppy floated. Kay placed the arrangement toward one end of the table, to balance a Japanese print above the other end.

On the mantel Kay had her dried arrangement. The dominant gesture was created by a twisted piece of driftwood. It writhed upward from among five pine cones and three stalks of bayberry. The container was gray-green and low.

Now that the dining room had been done over, in chartreuse and muted eggplant, Kay used a pewter bowl on the buffet, with "wooden roses" and rhododendron leaves. On the table she had a large wooden leaf bearing a pineapple, three artichokes, and five red onions. These were everyday arrangements; on the day when the club met with her, Kay used more exotic material, such as dead-men's-fingers (sponges), and unborn palm.

The scarcity of flowers in Kay's arrangements was compensated for by an abundance of flowers in pictures on the walls. There were great Van Gogh sunflowers in the living room, and flowers in the

"Blue Vase" of Cezanne, and flowers in the glass paperweight collection that caught the light there on the glass shelves in the dining-room bay window, between various succulent-leaved and spiny-leaved foliage plants.

The dimmed light resulting from the Venetian blinds was just right for Kay's specialty, African violets. But the Venetian blinds had to go, in favor of draw drapes. The new picture window cut into the wing would have given a good sunny spot for house plants, but there had to be a lamp in the window, and besides, when the sun shone, the room became unbearable if the drapes were not drawn.

There was an abundance of ivy and philodendron around, in the various objects that had been converted into "planters." The old sugar scoop on the wall had ivy in it, as did the lamp made out of an old coffee mill. There was no place for plants in the big lamp made out of a churn, or the one made out of a candle mold, or the pair that had been wallpaper rollers, or in the book ends made out of horseshoes and stirrups, but there was a foliage plant on the magazine table made out of a cobbler's bench, and there was a copper pot of ivy suspended from each end of the old oxbow yoke on one wall. There was ivy in the lamp on the bedside table, where "The Egg and I" was covered by "The Mature Mind" on Kay's side, and "Peace of Mind" covered "Five Acres and Independence" on Don's side.

Kay stopped bringing flowers into the bedroom after she had painted the furniture with Pennsylvania Dutch motifs full of tulips and birds and hex signs.

Kay and Don have only one child, named Sharon. But they have two boxer dogs named Stockwell Stillwater Hamlet and Stockwell Stillwater Ophelia.

Sharon is growing up. She will no doubt have several children, probably four. The style in size of family has changed just lately.

Only the white pine tree, the bleeding heart, the apple tree, the fern-leaved peony, and the Christmas cactus have seen all the ways in which the old house has been stylish.

REFERENCES

1. *Our Times: The United States, 1900–1925,* by Mark Sullivan. Scribner, New York, 1932.
2. *A Treatise on the Theory and Practice of Landscape Gardening, Adapted to North America; with a View to the Improvement of Country Residences . . . with Remarks on Rural Architecture,* by Andrew Jackson Downing. A. O. Moore and Company, New York, 1859.
2. *Handbook of Practical Landscape Gardening Designed for City and Suburban Residences, and Country Schoolhouses, Containing Designs for Lots and Grounds* by Franklin Reuben Elliott. D. M. Dewey, Rochester, New York, 1877.
4. *Old Time Gardens Newly Set Forth* by Alice Morse Earle. Macmillan, New York, 1901.
5. *A History of Horticulture in America to 1860* by U. P. Hedrick, Oxford, New York, 1950.
6. *The Story of Gardening,* by Richardson Wright. Garden City Publishing Co., New York, 1938.
7. *Life in America,* by Marshall B. Davidson. Houghton Mifflin Company, Boston, 1951.

INDEX

221